INTERACTION OF MATTER & ENERGY

INQUIRY IN PHYSICAL SCIENCE

INTERACTION SCIENCE CURRICULUM PROJECT

Norman Abraham

Patrick Balch

Donald Chaney

Lawrence M. Rohrbaugh

RAND McNALLY & COMPANY • Chicago

Printed in U. S. A.

A RAND McNALLY SCIENCE CURRICULUM PROJECT

First printing, July, 1968

Second printing, September, 1968

Third printing, June, 1969

Fourth printing, July, 1970

Authors

NORMAN ABRAHAM

Science Curriculum Consultant, Yuba City Unified School District, Yuba City, California. Mr. Abraham was Associate Director of the Biological Sciences Curriculum Study from 1964 to 1966. He contributed to the three versions of BSCS Biology and serves as supervisor of the BSCS Second Course.

PATRICK BALCH

Chairman Science Department, Yuba City High School, Yuba City, California. Mr. Balch was co-author of the BSCS Second Course and served on the BSCS evaluation and Film Committees.

DONALD CHANEY

Physics and Chemistry Teacher, Los Gatos High School, Los Gatos, California. Mr. Chaney has had extensive experience in teaching PSSC Physics and CHEM Chemistry.

LAWRENCE M. ROHRBAUGH

Professor of Botany, University of Oklahoma, Norman, Oklahoma. Dr. Rohrbaugh serves on the BSCS Steering Committee and was co-author of the BSCS Second Course. He has helped to implement the BSCS Yellow Version in India.

Consultants

ARNOLD B. GROBMAN

Dean: Rutgers College
Rutgers University, New Brunswick, New Jersey

PAUL DeH. HURD

Professor of Education: School of Education
Stanford University, Stanford, California

ADDISON E. LEE

Director: Science Education Center
University of Texas, Austin, Texas

FRANK OPPENHEIMER

Professor of Physics: Department of Physics and Astrophysics
University of Colorado, Boulder, Colorado

STANLEY WILLIAMSON

Chairman: Department of Science Education
Oregon State University, Corvallis, Oregon

Test Evaluation

HULDA GROBMAN, Professor of Secondary Education:
School of Education, New York University, New York, New York

Rand McNally

William B. Miller, Project Editor   John Gundlach, Associate Editor
Ellen Blackman, Copy Editor

Illustrators

Robert Flori, H/W Design, Chicago, Illinois   Larry Frederick, Glenview, Illinois
Curtis Clowdus, Weaverville, California

Foreword

Vast improvements are occurring in science education today. One of the most significant features is that new instructional materials are being developed coöperatively by experienced classroom teachers and university research scientists working together as teams. Such teams bring to the production of materials substantial knowledge about the children to be taught as well as a considerable expertise in the subject matter.

Another aspect of this new trend is the thorough trial use of the materials in actual classroom situations before release for publication. Through this procedure, preliminary copies of the teaching materials are tested for one or more school years by a number of teachers in a variety of classroom situations across the nation. Thus, before they are finally released for general use, the materials have undergone a truly experimental program of critical evaluation and development.

Interaction of Matter and Energy was produced in this fashion. The authors worked together as a writing team for several years on this particular set of materials and prepared experimental editions which were used in classrooms throughout the country. The trial program led to very substantial improvement in recasting the materials into their present form. In my opinion, this is the best possible method for the preparation of instructional materials for our schools.

Of additional significance is the fact that *Interaction of Matter and Energy* was designed specifically to articulate with the new secondary school science programs which have been developed recently with federal support and are being used very extensively. The writing team is thoroughly conversant with the new mathematics and science curricula; indeed some of its members have themselves been active participants in the development of such science programs.

Interaction of Matter and Energy proceeds from the simple to the complex; it develops a science of investigation and curiosity in the student; it provides no pat answers in a field that is changing rapidly; and it is both interesting and comprehensible to students in our junior high schools.

It is incumbent upon all of us to help today's students develop an understanding of the attitudes, processes, and goals of science; mastery of traditional content is not enough. Fortunately, the materials available for science instruction are better now than they have ever been before. Whether or not a particular student using this book is likely to become a scientist is not very important. More important is the fact that all students using this book are destined to live in an age in which an understanding of science will be essential. I am sure *Interaction of Matter and Energy* will serve these students well at their present level of schooling.

ARNOLD B. GROBMAN
Dean, Rutgers College
Director, Biological Sciences Curriculum Study, 1959–1965

Preface to Student

You are about to begin the study of a new science course—*Interaction of Matter and Energy*. Most of your class time will be spent in laboratory sessions: conducting investigations, collecting and interpreting data, and drawing conclusions that are entirely your own. In other words, most of the time you will be *doing* something rather than just reading about it or listening to your teacher talk about it. This is the way a scientist must work. If answers to all problems were known or immediately available, there would be no need for further research and investigation.

The teaching of science is undergoing a great change—almost a revolution—and you are being asked to participate. You will study many aspects of chemistry and physics that were at one time reserved for students in the eleventh or twelfth grade: the behavior of atoms and molecules, a study of the periodic chart of the elements, many of the basic laws of physics, and the significance of the physical sciences to life itself. The course is designed to end where physical science interacts with biological science.

You will come to understand that science is not just a collection of facts. Rather, science is continuing search for truth, with a bewildering number of false paths to take if one is not trained to be observant, cautious, and willing to use his own imagination and skill.

Science is a creative activity. For this reason you will be working in laboratory situations that should allow you to be as creative as possible—situations that should cause you to avoid accepting something as fact just because someone said it is so. Keep in mind that only 70 years ago the concept of air travel was regarded as the silly notion of unbalanced minds. Yet at this very moment, plans are under way for producing aircraft that will travel at a rate of two thousand miles per hour. Passengers will be able to cross the Atlantic Ocean in about an hour and a half.

Biologists now talk of the possible existence of life on other planets, of learning to understand what lies in the depths of the oceans, and of creating artificial parts to replace vital organs in the human body. These advances depend heavily on the development of the physical sciences: chemistry, physics, geology, and astronomy. You will be challenged throughout this course to understand basic principles of physical science that will prepare you to live in an era of rapid scientific advancement.

Maintaining a careful record of your laboratory work will be an essential part of studying this course. Frequently you will be asked to make notes during an investigation or to organize and record data. From your notes you should be able to interpret the results of an investigation and to predict what should happen if you carried out an experiment in a certain way. Scientists call such predictions *hypotheses*. Forming hypotheses and testing them experimentally are among the many scientific skills you will use. Finally the authors hope you will enjoy this course and would be pleased to receive your comments at any time during your study of *Interaction of Matter and Energy*.

THE AUTHORS

June 15, 1968

Acknowledgments

The original design for *Interaction of Matter and Energy* was outlined in 1959 by a group of junior high school science teachers who had been gradually substituting their own written materials for the conventional texts then in use. During each subsequent year these materials were modified on the basis of student response and exchange of ideas within and outside the group. As the major curriculum studies in science emerged, the *Interaction* program was further modified to reflect the philosophy and goals of BSCS biology, PSSC physics, and CHEM and CBA chemistry.

In 1965 the first experimental editions of IME were distributed to trial teachers in 40 schools. The materials—lab texts, teacher's editions, and achievement tests—were used in the classroom with approximately 4000 students during the 1965–1966 school year. Teachers' evaluations of content and student achievement were submitted to the authors and editors. At the conclusion of this and succeeding trial years, revisions suggested by teachers, students, and consultants were reviewed by the writing team, which included a number of trial teachers. Experimental editions were revised accordingly. The 1966–1967 trial was conducted with more than 200 teachers and 18,000 students. During the final trial year, 1967–1968, more than 400 teachers and 37,000 students participated in an evaluation of the experimental quarterly and final examinations. These, too, were revised. Thus, IME is the result of three years of classroom testing and revision in an attempt to improve the teaching of physical science. Many teachers and students have contributed directly to this program, and it is impossible to list all who have assisted in other ways. Indirectly, but significantly, the many science consultants, coordinators, supervisors, principals, and other educators who arranged briefing sessions for IME teachers made possible a sufficiently broad and critical trial.

Special thanks is due Mr. George Buonocore, Chairman of the Science Department, Prospect High School, Campbell, California, for his assistance in reviewing supplementary materials listed in student and teacher editions.

Table of contents

x

SECTION ELEVEN: HEAT ENERGY 207

SECTION TWELVE: OBSERVING THE BEHAVIOR OF LIGHT 225

SECTION THIRTEEN: OBSERVING THE NATURE OF WAVES 245

SECTION FOURTEEN: ENERGY CONVERSION 253

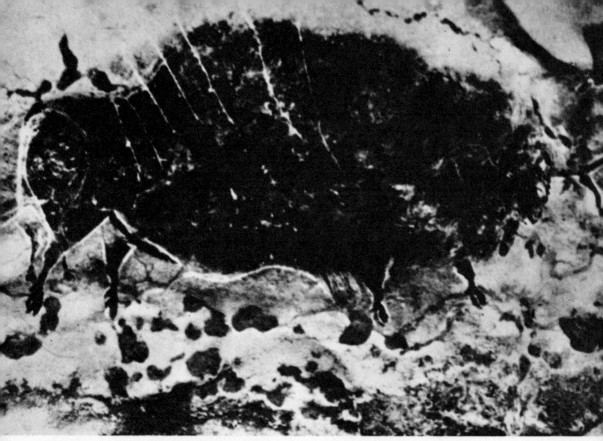

Fernand Windels, *Lascaux Cave Paintings*, Faber & Faber, Ltd., 1949

Figure 1 · 1. Drawing of a prehistoric bison by Cro-Magnon man, from a cave near Lascaux, France. The drawing is about 4 feet 6 inches long, painted in reddish-brown and black. It appears that seven spears were scratched over the flank of the bison.

A Way to Begin

Drawings on the walls of ancient caves near Lascaux, France, and Altamira, Spain, suggest that early cave dwellers recorded some of their observations and experiences (Figure 1·1). These *could* represent some of the earliest recorded "scientific" observations.

Suppose we imagine that twenty-five thousand years ago a Cro-Magnon man was telling the children of the tribe about his experiences on a hunt. He may have used some drawings to show how to kill a running bison. The hunter aimed his spear a certain distance ahead of the animal so that bison and spear would reach the same spot at the same time.

At first Cro-Magnon man probably learned successful hunting methods by trial and error. Because failure to kill bison meant going without food, the need to improve hunting technique was vital. To succeed, the hunter learned to aim ahead of the running bison—to throw his spear toward a point where no real target existed at the time. If incorrectly aimed, the spear would miss the animal or cause only a minor wound. In either case, the bison would escape.

Perhaps the hunter recorded his data, using the wall of a cave as his notebook. His "students" could then ask questions: Why does a bison usually survive when a spear pierces its hind quarter?

Figure 1 · 2. Cro-Magnon hunters and prehistoric bison.

Why does a bison usually die when a spear pierces its front quarter? What is so vital about the front of the bison? Is its "life" located in only one spot? Answers to these questions might have led to additional drawings (Figures 1·3 and 1·4). One drawing might have shown a spear piercing the front quarter of a bison; another, a spear piercing the hind quarter. The drawings may have been the work of one man, but perhaps the observations were taken from the experiences of many hunters.

Figure 1 · 3. Wounded bison.

Figure 1 · 4. Dying bison with spear in the region of the heart.

For this story we can, of course, draw only from imagination. Cro-Magnon man may not have used his drawings as a means of instruction. Indeed, some researchers think that the cave drawings were used entirely for magic and rituals. We will probably never know the exact purpose of these drawings, since there is no written history on which we can base our interpretations.

The drawings on the walls of ancient caves do exist, however, and perhaps in a crude way early man did use what we call a "scientific approach." If he attempted to explain why a spear in the chest of the bison, near the heart, was more likely to kill the animal than a spear in its hind quarter, we could say he was acting like a scientist.

Trying to Define Science

No one knows exactly when science began. Even if the earliest written descriptions of human activity were found, we would still be a long way from the beginning of science. Writing and record-keeping developed long after man began observing and thinking about his surroundings. But because science is a special kind of *human* activity, at least we can say that science began some time after man appeared on earth.

Because science is a *special* kind of activity, we cannot say it began when man first thought, or when he first looked at a rock, a tree, or the sun. He may have done these things for many thousands of years before he thought or did something scientifically.

Notice, also, that we say science is a kind of *activity*—not just a body of knowledge. What do we mean by scientific activity? by scientific thinking (which is a very important kind of activity)? You could read many books about science, its history, and its achievements. You might come to understand what we mean by saying that science is a special kind of activity. But to learn what science is just by *reading* about it would take a very long time—years, perhaps.

Maybe a more direct way to understand science is to *do* what a scientist does. This course is designed so that you will spend most of your time doing things—investigating—rather than reading. How scientific your investigations are will depend on your interest and care in observing, recording data, interpreting results, and drawing conclusions. These are basic scientific skills, and they are used by the professional scientist no matter how simple or how complicated the question he seeks to answer.

As this course proceeds you will find that science involves many methods—that it is a complex activity which cannot be described in a single sentence, paragraph, or chapter. There is no one scientific method that can be used in all cases. The method that is used depends on the problem or question, and on the investigator.

Though science is complex, the popular notion that scientific work requires huge laboratories and vast amounts of complicated apparatus is often incorrect. Much of the creative work in science is performed with little more than the natural senses, an inquiring mind, and (perhaps) a pencil and paper.

The scientist does not take his surroundings for granted. He seeks explanations for what he observes, no matter how commonplace the event. Now you will have an opportunity to observe a simple interaction of matter and energy. If you make an honest attempt to explain what you observe, you will be acting much like a professional scientist.

Getting Involved

Set up the apparatus shown in Figure 1·5. Almost any kind of support will do (chairs, ring stands, etc.). The objects hanging from the strings should weigh about 4 ounces each. Fishing weights, bolts, or other common objects may be used. The strings supporting the two objects should be about the same length, with enough distance between them to prevent the objects from hitting each other when they swing. Without bending the horizontal string, pull one of the objects toward you and release it. Observe carefully for two or three minutes and record what happens to each of the objects.

Figure 1 · 5.
Set-up of strings
and objects. What
effect will the
motion of one
object have
on the other?

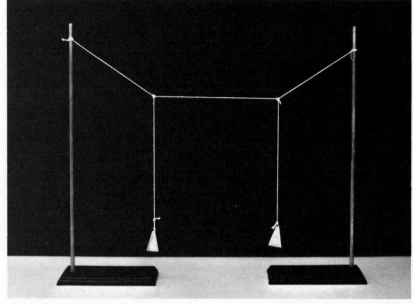

David Prall

You may find the behavior hard to explain. But where do you look for an explanation? First, you may attempt to build one on your own observations. Or you may simply decide to accept, without question, an explanation from someone else. The scientist requires that an explanation agree with what is observed. Your explanation for the behavior of the suspended objects must agree with all your observations.

Scientists often observe events they cannot immediately explain. Their observations may form the basis for explanation as they repeat experiments, try different arrangements, and make new observations. You will carry out these kinds of testing activities during the course. But you need not wait for the investigations which follow to gain such experience. Begin to test your explanation now. You might change the arrangement of the suspended objects, or change the number of objects suspended. You might use different weights, or change the lengths of the strings.

These investigations can and should be done at home. Perhaps later in the course you will be better able to explain the results of these investigations. But you can make many observations now—

and the more observations you make, the more confidence you will have in your explanation.

Through much of history, man has sought explanations for his observations. When observations have been too limited, his explanations often have been incomplete or even wrong. Primitive men often used spirits—good or evil—to explain events for which they could find no visible causes. In the cultures of American Indians, for example, many events in nature were believed to be the work of spirits. Among primitive tribes of Africa, the Amazon, Australia, New Guinea, and other regions, evil spirits are blamed for floods, droughts, disease, and earthquakes. Good spirits are given credit for a large crop or for the recovery of a sick person.

Figure 1 · 6. Before the arrival of the Spanish, in the sixteenth century, the Inca civilization of South America worshiped the sun as the source of all power and the cause of all events beyond the control of man. How might the Incas have come to believe this? In what ways were their observations more limited than those of modern man?

The Modern Scientific Community

For thousands of years, people of many countries and races have been observing, investigating, and developing theories about their surroundings. Much of our present knowledge is the result of the work of early Egyptians, Chinese, Romans, Greeks, Arabs, and many others (Figures 1 · 7–1 · 11).

Modern science, too, is international. We have great advantages which the ancients did not have. Our means of recording and communicating spoken or written information are much more rapid and more accurate. An announcement of a new scientific discovery, idea, or method may spread around the world by radio and television within minutes. Air transportation makes it possible for scientists to attend international conventions or to visit the laboratories of other scientists anywhere in the world.

For today's scientific community, distances and (in most cases) national boundaries no longer present obstacles to the movement of men and information. In somewhat the same way, the major branches of science—chemistry, physics, biology, astronomy, and so on—are no longer separated by distinct boundaries. Neither is there a sharp dividing line between science and the many branches of *technology*—those fields in which the sciences are applied, such as engineering and medicine. All branches of science and technology are related, some very closely. In the twentieth century an overlapping of interests and skills has resulted from the increasing complexity of scientific work and the problems that scientists have been asked to solve. Examples of such enormous problems are not hard to find: pollution of the earth's water and atmosphere, the population explosion, the need for vast new energy resources. Finally, consider our efforts in the exploration of space. Using knowledge developed by scientists, engineers design and develop rockets and fuels. Physical scientists use the rockets to collect information about the earth's atmosphere and the space beyond. Biologists make sure that conditions within rockets are safe; and they are interested in the possibility of life on other planets. Each group must coöperate with and depend upon the skills of men in other fields of specialization.

Figure 1 · 7. This painting from the wall of an Egyptian tomb shows metal-workers heating gold ore and pouring off molten metal into casting molds.

Figure 1 · 8. Roman engineers designed aqueducts to carry water from springs to far-off cities. The water flowed through a trough above the arches.

Culver Pictures

Figure 1 · 9. Laboratory of a sixteenth-century alchemist. The alchemist's techniques often resembled those of modern science, but his efforts to convert common metals into gold were unsuccessful.

Culver Pictures

Figure 1 · 10. The Chinese invented gunpowder and used it in several kinds of weapons. Here a warrior is rocketing arrows toward the enemy.

Herb Comess

Figure 1 · 11. Uses of numbers are endless in this age of huge quantities and precise measure. Modern numbers combine symbols and systems developed by the Arabs, Persians, Egyptians, and Hindus.

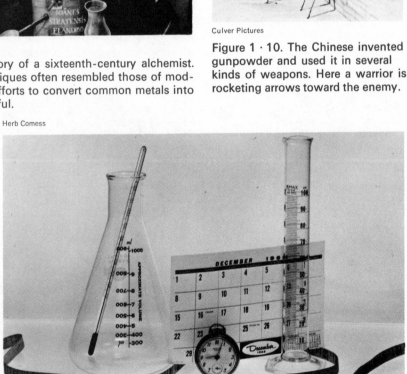

The possibility of life on other planets captures the imagination of young and old alike. Whether or not we find answers to questions about life on other planets depends on how well we use our skills and knowledge. We *can* say that the search for knowledge about our surroundings is not one guided solely by physicists, chemists, biologists, astronomers, or engineers. It demands the best in ability from specialists in all areas of human activity and learning. Through coöperative effort, we may someday understand what lies beyond our earthly environment.

Of course, few of us will play any direct role in the exploration of space. Unless you plan to pursue a career in physics, chemistry, biology, or a related field, you may wonder how the study of science can be of any value. There are several answers worth considering.

First, science offers an opportunity for you to exercise your curiosity and to practice sound reasoning. Defining and working out a problem can be fun. And skills in doing so can be useful in all creative fields—in the arts, in business, in public service, to name a few. Second, science provides a view of the natural world that is necessary to every well-informed person. A citizen who lacks understanding of the basic processes and principles of science may find it difficult to make intelligent decisions about certain important issues that can affect his community or the entire nation. Flood control, conservation of wildlife, the exploration of space, pollution of air and water, research in medicine—these and a hundred other needs will call for the time, effort, and money of our society. And the voter will be asked, in many cases, to decide which problems are most important.

Today man has the power to shape the content and conditions of his surroundings. Science has provided a great deal of this power. But without support from well-informed citizens, the scientific community cannot continue its work. Without guidance from the public, science may fail to meet our most pressing needs. Finally, without a basic understanding of the methods and goals of science, the people of a nation may fail to use their resources wisely and to preserve the environment for themselves and for the next generations.

Culver Pictures

Marie Curie (1864–1934), a Pole, isolated a radio-active element, which she named radium.

Culver Pictures

Bettmann Archive

Sir Isaac Newton (1642–1727), an Englishman, formulated the laws of gravitation and motion.

Wilhelm Konrad Röntgen (1845–1923), a German, discovered the X-ray.

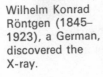

Harris & Ewing

George Washington Carver (1864–1943), an American Negro, whose experiments with peanuts, pecans, and sweet potatoes helped agricultural progress in the South.

Keystone Press

Enrico Fermi (1901–1954), an Italian, helped create the first atomic pile.

Keystone Press

Hideki Yukawa (1907–   ), a Japanese, predicted the existence of mesons, nuclear particles much heavier than electrons.

Figure 1 · 12. Scientists of all races and many nationalities have increased man's understanding of the world, the forces that affect it, and the uses of its resources.

PROBLEMS

1. Write a short statement which either supports or refutes each of the following ideas.
   a. Science began with cave paintings.
   b. The cave paintings in France and Spain are some of the earliest records of scientific activities.
   c. Science began with the use of tools.
   d. Science began with mathematics.
2. Suggest other uses prehistoric man may have had for his cave drawings.
3. How do you think people will react if scientists find fossils on the moon? Would this be evidence that the moon was once a part of the earth?
4. Suggest some examples of investigations that might require coöperation among men in several branches of science.

REFERENCES

Asimov, Isaac. *The New Intelligent Man's Guide to Science.* New York: Basic Books, 1965.

————. *Breakthroughs in Science.* Boston: Houghton Mifflin Co., 1959.

Baumann, Hans. *The Caves of the Great Hunters.* New York: Pantheon Books, 1962.

Dampier, Sir William Cecil. *A History of Science.* 4th ed. London: Cambridge University Press, 1949.

Holton, Gerald, and Roller, Duane. *Foundations of Modern Physical Science.* Reading, Mass.: Addison-Wesley Publishing Co., Inc., 1958.

Scheele, William E. *The Cave Hunters.* New York: World Publishing Co., 1959.

Structure of Matter: A Model

Matter may be defined as anything that takes up space and has weight. Our natural senses of sight, touch, hearing, taste, and smell provide us with evidence that matter exists as mountains, oceans, clouds, cabbages, pigs, and so on. But our senses alone do not permit us to see how matter is constructed or to know how it behaves.

Man has wondered about the structure of matter for thousands of years. Until a few hundred years ago, he had to rely on his natural senses and on opinions to explain the structure and behavior of matter. Microscopes, telescopes, and most other kinds of scientific instruments did not exist. The idea of experimenting to seek answers to questions was not an accepted procedure. In spite of these limitations, man's curiosity caused him to observe, wonder about, and make interpretations about matter.

A Greek teacher, Democritus (470–400 B.C.), used the word *atom* to describe what he thought was the smallest unit of matter. There was, according to Democritus, empty space between atoms. They might differ in shape and size, but all atoms were made of the same kind of "stuff."

In the schools of Democritus' time, teachers and groups of students often walked about together, informally discussing problems, asking questions, and forming theories about the nature of man and the physical world. Imagine that while Democritus was walking with his students he picked up a dried leaf, crushed it in his hand, and said, "This leaf is composed of many things. After I crush it, I am still holding pieces of the original leaf. If I crush it further, I will still be holding pieces of the leaf, even though they look and feel like dust. The smallest pieces are composed of particles so small we cannot see them. These I call atoms."

Democritus' ideas about atoms were almost lost to future generations because Aristotle (384–322 B.C.) rejected them. Aristotle, one of the greatest Greek writers and philosophers, adopted an older concept of matter, which assumed the existence of four elements: fire, water, earth, and air. These four, and various combinations of them, were thought to form all the different substances on earth and in the heavens.

Aristotle's influence lasted for many centuries, affecting European thought and society through Medieval times. Though his writings represented a lifetime of observation, curiosity, and debate, they were accepted without much question by generations following. Few would have thought it proper to test Aristotle's assumptions and conclusions about matter and the physical world.

A great revolution in science occurred when experimental *testing* became the accepted procedure. Today, we expect evidence. No scientist can set himself up as an authority without showing that his ideas are supported by tests—tests that can be repeated by others and that will produce the same results.

Although the word *atom* is useful today in talking about the structure of matter, no one has ever seen atoms. Our acceptance of the existence of atoms depends upon many different kinds of evidence. We *could* assume that all properties of matter arise from some other cause, such as the activities of demons.[1] We would then have two theories, and either one might be used to explain the behavior of matter. The "atomic theory" can be used to seek an explanation for the behavior of matter in matter itself. The "demon theory" can be used to explain this behavior on the basis

---

[1] You may prefer to use a different name, such as "gremlin."

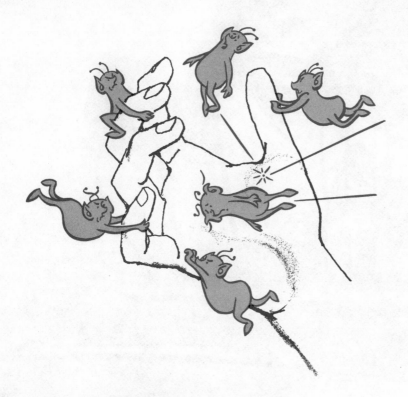

Figure 2 · 1.
A possible explanation for pressure against a moving hand.

of something acting on matter from the outside.

The terms *demon* or *gremlin* can be useful in understanding the nature of science. For example, if you put your hand out the window of a rapidly moving automobile, a force pushes your hand backwards. What is this force? It *could* be caused by thousands of invisible demons pushing against your hand (Figure 2·1). If the car stops, you no longer feel the force. Perhaps demons push only against something that is moving.

You probably would not agree that this force is caused by demons. You might say your hand is forced backwards because it is pushing against air, and that air is the force—not demons. But so far the evidence could be used to support both theories. You have no good reason to reject either one.

The idea of demons (or any alternative) can be useful. Think of demons as being responsible for a certain event, and attempt to find evidence that supports this explanation. Then see if the same evidence can be used to support a different theory.

Figure 2 · 2. Could the effects shown here be explained in terms of demons? If so, would the demon model used to explain Figure 2 · 1 need to be changed? In what way?

This method will be used a number of times throughout the course. You will be asked to interpret an observation in terms of demons or some other cause. Then you should select the explanation that is best supported by evidence gathered from your investigations. Seeking the best explanation for something you observe is an important part of science.

You are not being asked to believe in the existence of the demons described in this book. You should realize, however, that words like "atom," "molecule," or "demon" do not *explain* anything. Therefore you will be asked to tell what atoms must be like if they are used to explain the behavior of matter. You also will be asked to explain the same behavior by describing the powers demons must have if they are the cause of this behavior.

Observation and Interpretation

When a scientist says that something is "true," he usually means that available evidence supports a *model* he has constructed. The model makes it possible for him to relate certain observations, experimental results, and data to one another. Scientists use the term *model* in a much different sense than most of us do in ordinary speech. We talk about model airplanes, model behavior, or fashion models. None of these fits the idea of a scientific model very well. The kind of model the scientist uses is a *mental image*. It may be based partly on past evidence and accepted facts; it may be based partly on theories; and it may be based partly on opinions, guesses, or hunches. If possible, a scientist will want to construct a physical, visible copy of the model he has in his mind, and this may make it easier for him to communicate his ideas to others. But the model in his mind may be too complicated to construct. For example, imagine trying to construct a complete model of the universe, which includes billions of stars. Or the mental model might be based on a process that extends over great lengths of time—the evolution of mammals, for example. Perhaps speeds, distances, and temperatures involved in the model cannot be created or copied in a physical model. In any case, the model, whether it can be copied or not, exists in the mind of the scientist.

How are models useful? Many scientific models allow man to organize past and present experimental results into a logical pattern. A good model fits together all the available evidence. Then, if someone finds new evidence that does not fit the model, the model must be changed—or perhaps even discarded in favor of another model. Consider again a model designed to show the structure of the universe—one that includes all that is known or suspected about the number, size, and movement of stars and planets. According to this model, it is supposed that there are many planetary systems throughout the universe. Each system has a star or "sun" as its center, and each sun may have planets orbiting around it. In our part of the universe there are millions of stars, or suns. Telescopes show that this model appears to be true for our own solar system, but we can only *assume* that it is true for distant regions of the vast universe, where planets, moons, or suns cannot yet be observed or detected. Thus, our model may change as we develop new ways of exploring, observing, or *thinking* about the universe.

Consider our own planet. Geologists have constructed several models to help us visualize what the structure of the earth may be like. Though no one has yet observed what lies beneath the very thin crust of our planet, geologists use models to show what they think the interior of the earth is like (Figure 2 · 3).

Other examples of scientific models may be found in biology— the study of living things. Biologists use a model to explain how certain traits are passed from parent to offspring. With this model they are able to make useful predictions, even though the actual process represented by the model occurs on such a small scale that it cannot be seen.

On the other hand, something is not easy to understand just because it is easy to observe. We might find models helpful in seeking explanations for visible but unfamiliar events. Suppose you observe an animal of a kind you have never before seen, stealthily moving across a grassy field. You might explain its behavior by saying that the animal is hungry. Actually you have no way of knowing what the feelings of the animal are. You use your own familiar feeling of hunger as a model to explain the actions of the animal. Your explanation might be called the "hunger model" for this animal's behavior.

A different explanation for the behavior might be a "fear model," based on the assumption that the animal is attempting to find a place to hide—perhaps from hunters, perhaps from other animals. The "hunger model" predicts that the animal's behavior would change if it found food. The "fear model" predicts that the animal's behavior would change if it reached some bushes or a

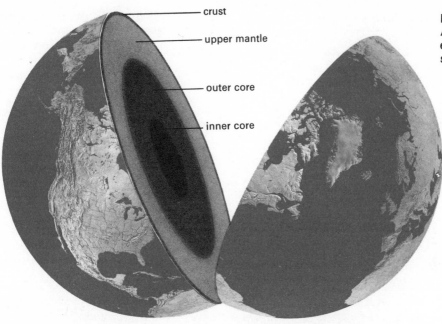

crust

upper mantle

outer core

inner core

Figure 2 · 3.
A model of the
earth's interior
structure.

dense woods. Both models allow you to make predictions. And the predictions can then be tested so that you can finally accept or reject your original explanation of the animal's behavior.

Perhaps we should look at one more example before turning to atoms and molecules again. Imagine a boy living in a small valley near the ocean. Until he has traveled out of the valley, his model of the world might resemble a large bowl. If he moved up to the ridge, he might get the idea that the earth is like a plate with some uneven places in it, but extending out in all directions and on the whole rather flat. If he moved down to the seashore and watched ships sail away, he might change his model again, so that it resembled a bowl turned upside down. In this way he could explain the gradual disappearance of the ships. If he saw pictures of the earth taken from a rocket, he might change his model of the earth to resemble a ball.

As you continue, keep in mind that a model is a mental picture of what something is supposed to be like. And if the model is scientific, it must be revised when it is not in agreement with all evidence. A model in science is a mental device that allows us to

NASA

Figure 2 · 4. The curvature of the earth is clearly visible in this photograph
taken from the Gemini XI spacecraft at an altitude of 540 nautical miles.
The large land mass is India.

organize observations and experimental results into a useful
pattern. Notice that we say *useful*. Such a model must also be
consistent—that is, it must allow us to fit all evidence together
logically. This does not mean the model is truth in the sense that it
is a fact or something that can be observed. If observation or
experiments do not support a model, the model may be changed
or replaced by one that better agrees with the observations and
experimental evidence.

You have some evidence to indicate that atoms are particles;

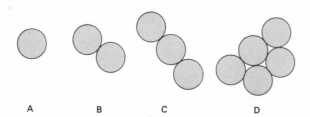

Figure 2 · 5.
(A) Model of an
atom. (B,C,D)
Models of
molecules.

but you do not have any way of knowing what the shape of an atom is. Lacking evidence, why not choose a simple and convenient model—a circle (Figure 2 · 5A)? Two or more atoms joined together form what is called a *molecule* (Figures 2 · 5B, C, D). Atoms may combine to form large molecules (Figures 2 · 6A, B). On the other hand, large molecules may be broken apart to form smaller molecules or individual atoms.

It is not as easy to draw a model representing energy. But we can use a *word* model: *Whenever some kind of activity is taking place, energy is present.*

The purpose of the investigations you are about to perform is to allow you to make some observations about the behavior of matter. You will be asked to gather the observations, organize them, interpret them, and, from this information, build a model that will help you in understanding the structure and behavior of matter.

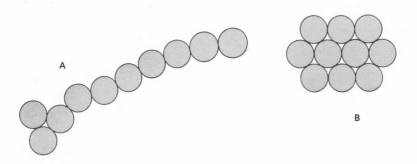

Figure 2 · 6.
Atoms in larger
molecules may
be arranged in
chains (A) or in
clusters (B).

During your investigations, it is important that you make a clear distinction between what you see (observation) and the meaning you draw from it (interpretation). Your observation of the movement of the sun relative to the earth is the same as the observations made by men hundreds of years ago. Yet you believe the earth moves around the sun, while they believed that the sun moves around the earth. See Figures 2 · 7 and 2 · 8 for the ancient and modern models of the solar system.

Figure 2 · 7. This relationship of the earth to the sun, the moon, and all known planets was widely accepted for more than a thousand years after it appeared in 150 A.D.

Figure 2 · 8. A modern model of the solar system. Compare this model with Figure 2 · 7. Sizes and distances are not to scale.

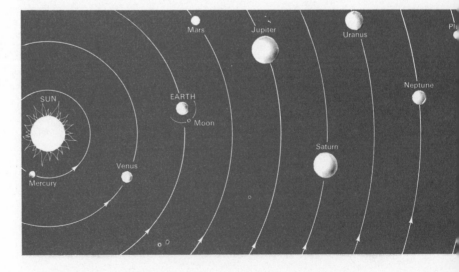

PROBLEMS

1. It is often difficult to decide whether a "fact" is based on observation or on interpretation. For example, highway police often check for speed violations by laying a "detector wire" across the road. Instruments attached to the wire record the impact of each vehicle's front wheels and rear wheels as they cross the wire. The time elapsed between front- and rear-wheel impacts is then indicated. Whenever the time elapsed is less than a certain interval, it is accepted as fact that the vehicle is speeding. Is such a "fact" based on observation or interpretation? Give reasons for your answer.

2. What is your opinion of each of the following statements?
    a. It is quite proper to honor the opinions of those who have studied a subject thoroughly. But it is not reasonable to accept, without question or doubt, statements of fact as representing absolute truth.
    b. It is important to distinguish between intelligent doubt —which may deserve investigation—and a demand for "proof" in every case. For instance, it is reasonable to accept as fact that if a person steps in front of a speeding automobile he will be killed or badly injured.
    c. Seeing is believing.

3. What kind of model do you think Democritus might have used to describe atoms?

Observations on the Behavior of Matter

The atomic-molecular model used by scientists to explain the structure and behavior of matter is based on some of the same observations, investigations, and interpretations that you will make. The incredibly small, invisible world of atomic particles presents a difficult problem because we cannot get at it or even see it. We have the same problem, of course, with seeing and understanding what occurs in distant parts of the universe, which are beyond the reach of our most powerful telescopes and the fastest spaceships now imagined. For this reason a useful model of the structure of matter is necessary. We cannot see atoms or molecules. Yet we must find some way to account for the appearance and behavior of matter. Let us begin the same way a scientist would—by observing and investigating matter.

Figure 2 · 9. Electron microscopes enable scientists to see unbelievably small particles, structures, and organisms.
Abbott Laboratories

Figure 2 · 10. Particles of tobacco viru fied about 73,000 times under an electron micro
Virus Laboratory, University of California, Berkeley

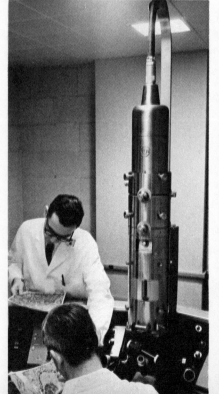

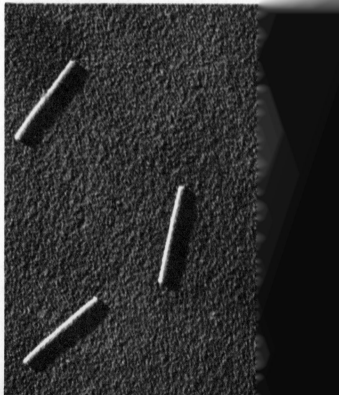

Figure 2 · 11. Though its average distance from the earth is about 900,000,000 miles, the planet Saturn and the satellite "rings" surrounding it can be greatly magnified with modern telescopes, making photographs like this possible.

Figure 2 · 12. Like the electron microscope, the telescope allows man to view objects and events far beyond the range of the naked eye.

INVESTIGATION 1: Estimating Size

The purpose of this investigation is to provide information that may be useful in making a rough estimate of the size of atoms or molecules. You will observe some very small pieces of matter. Remember that *looking* at small particles is observation; but *saying* that atoms must be a certain size is interpretation.

MATERIALS (per team)
    Chalk
    Plastic, metric/English ruler
    Hand lens
    Large, round, aluminum (pizza or pie) pan
    Finely powdered chalk (use in Procedure C)
    Chalkboard erasers
    Several toothpicks
    Liquid soap or detergent

PROCEDURES
A. How can you find the thickness of one page in your book? There are at least two methods you might use. One is much easier *and* more accurate than the other. Try both methods, and record the data in your notebook.
B. Crush a piece of chalk into fine particles. Place the ruler alongside the crushed chalk and view the particles and the ruler through your hand lens. Attempt to measure the size of the smallest particles of chalk you can see.

INTERPRETATIONS
1. Which did you find easier to measure—the thickness of a piece of paper or the size of a particle of chalk?
2. From your measurements of paper and chalk, make a general statement about the size of atoms or molecules.

PROCEDURES (continued)
C. Pour water into the aluminum pan until it is about half-full. Using the erasers and following your teacher's directions, cover

the surface of the water near the center of the dish with a *light* coating of chalk dust.

Predict what will happen if you add a droplet of soap to the dish of chalk-covered water. Record your prediction.

Dip the end of a clean toothpick into the liquid soap. Obtain a small droplet of soap on the point of the toothpick, and measure the *diameter* (distance across) of the droplet. Record the measurement in your notebook.

Carefully lower the droplet over the center of the dish until it just touches the chalky surface. Record your observations.

Measure the diameter of the droplet of soap after it has been added to the water.

INTERPRETATIONS (continued)

3. Was your prediction about what would happen to the droplet of soap correct?
4. Compare the diameter and volume of the droplet of soap before it was placed in the water with its diameter and volume after it was added to the water.

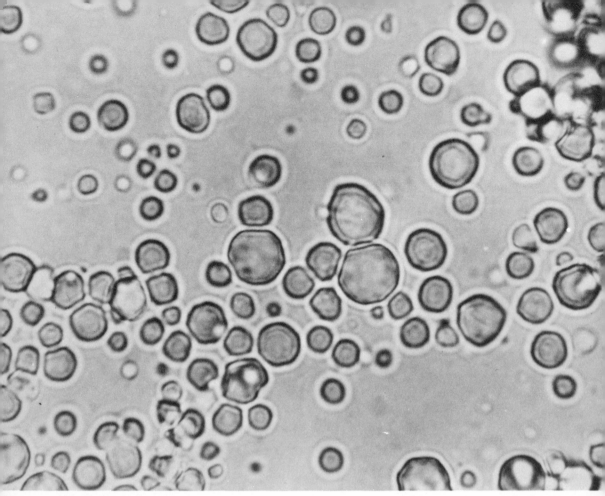

University of Oklahoma

Figure 2·13. This photomicrograph shows fat particles in milk magnified approximately 1400 times.

Motion of Particles

Your observations indicate that if matter is made up of small units, or atoms, these units must be smaller than the smallest pieces of chalk—so small that they cannot be directly observed. Other ideas about the nature of matter can be explored. Two major directions for our research are evident: One involves a study of the *structure* of small particles. The other involves a study of the *behavior* of these particles.

If you place a drop of homogenized milk (diluted 1 part milk to 3 parts water) on a glass slide and examine it under the high power of a microscope (400X or more) in strong light, you should see tiny particles. If you look closely, the particles can be seen to

Figure 2 · 14.
The presence of
demons could be
an explanation
for the motion
of particles.

move about in random, jerky motions, as though each particle had its own source of energy.

The continuous motion of these particles could be the actions of demons. You would have to assume that demons are smaller than the particles, or that demons are as transparent as the water—for the demons are not seen. Also there would have to be many demons present, each pushing or pulling on a particle to keep it continuously in motion. All observations indicate that the random, jerky motion of particles continues indefinitely; therefore, demons must have an endless source of energy! Or perhaps it is possible that demons are able to obtain their energy from the light shining upon them.

In fact, you are likely to suspect that something other than demons accounts for the continuous motion of the particles. But can you back up your idea with evidence?

PROBLEM

1. Try to describe models that could account for the continuous motion of the particles. Develop two arguments: one crediting demons with this activity, the other explaining the behavior of the particles in terms of the properties of atoms. Be as convincing and consistent as you can in developing both of these hypotheses.

Bubbles, Drops, and Films

Usually there is air both on the inside and on the outside of a soap bubble. The bubble itself is a very thin layer of liquid—a film. A soap bubble is a spherical film of water in which there is some dissolved soap.

A *drop* of liquid may be surrounded by air (or other gases) but its interior is all liquid. A drop of one liquid may be surrounded by another liquid, such as an oil drop in water.

Bubbles are fun to make and look at, but they also play a vital role in much more serious events and processes. Let us look at a few examples related to science and technology. An air bubble in the bloodstream can block the flow of blood, which could result in injury or even death. Bubbles formed during the manufacture of steel could result in a weak beam in a bridge or a faulty valve in a rocket engine.

The structure and behavior of drops, films, and bubbles may be described with a model that illustrates the structure and behavior of matter. Or you can assume that demons are responsible for the characteristics and activities of matter.

You have gathered information about the size and motion of some of the smallest particles of matter that can be seen. Now you will investigate the behavior of water particles. With the information gained from the investigations, attempt to construct a model to explain this behavior. Your work in later investigations should provide additional information which may increase your confidence in the model or which may cause you to change it.

INVESTIGATION 2: The Nature of Drops

MATERIALS (per team)

2 medicine droppers

Wax paper or plastic sheeting such as Saran Wrap or Baggies (about 4 x 8 inches)

4 toothpicks

Soap solution

30 ml of oil (vegetable, mineral, petroleum, or silicon)
2 beakers or jars (250-ml)
Paper towels

PROCEDURES

A. With a clean dropper, place several water droplets of different sizes on the wax paper. One droplet should be as small as possible, and the largest should be many times that size. Place various sized droplets on other surfaces, such as a piece of plastic sheeting, a table top, and a piece of paper towel.

B. Observe differences in the shapes of the drops, beginning with the smallest. Make sketches and record your observations.

C. Place two small drops of water on the plastic sheeting as close to each other as possible. Determine how close the two drops must be to each other before they interact. Record this interaction. What happens to the two drops when they touch?

D. Touch some of the droplets with the tip of a clean toothpick. Observe and record any change in appearance of the drops.

Herb Comess

Figure 2 · 15.
Set-up for
Procedure F.

E. Dip the tip of a clean toothpick into the soap solution. Touch a water drop with this toothpick. Repeat this procedure several times with other drops. Record your observations in your notebook.

F. Carefully introduce a few drops of water into a beaker about two-thirds full of a clear oil, as shown in Figure 2 · 15 on page 33. Describe the shape of these drops. Can you explain why they have this shape? What happens to these drops? Slowly squeeze the dropper until all the water has been forced into the vegetable oil. Do all the drops move at the same speed? Record your observations.

G. Follow the steps in Procedure F again, but this time use a dropper full of clear oil and a beaker of water. Describe and explain the results.

INTERPRETATIONS

The following questions may serve as guides in making interpretations, but do not feel limited by them. The value of this activity will depend on your ability to change, if necessary, the model you have developed to describe the behavior of water particles. The only requirement is that you support your statements with experimental evidence.

1. Why do you think drops take the shapes you observed?

2. What could make the shape of drops change with increasing size?

3. Does the material or surface on which a droplet is placed affect the droplet in any way? If you found that different surfaces have different effects, try to explain the result in each case.

4. What statement can you make about the behavior of two water drops when they touch?

5. How did the shape of the droplets change when touched with a clean toothpick? with a toothpick dipped into the soap solution? Explain your answers.

6. From the information obtained in these experiments what general statement can you make that would support the concept of demons? In what ways can your observations support some other model relating to the behavior of drops?

INVESTIGATION 3: The Nature of a Film

In Investigation 2 you observed surfaces of drops, rather than entire drops. Often in science (and in mathematics) it is useful to consider what might be called an extreme case. Therefore, why not examine a "drop" that has the characteristic of being almost all surface—an extremely flat drop? A soap film has this desired characteristic and is the subject of this investigation.

MATERIALS (per team)
    Thread
    Wire frames (Figure 2 · 16)
    Soap solution
    Large beaker or pan for soap solution
    Several toothpicks
    Small plastic or glass funnel

Figure 2 · 16. Wire frames to be used in Procedures A–C.

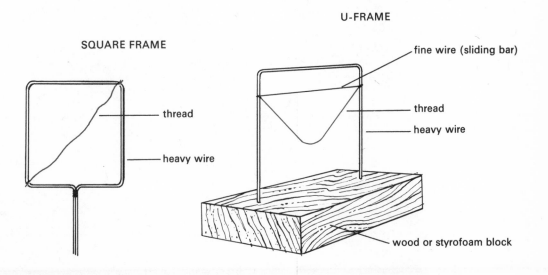

PROCEDURES

A. Tie a piece of thread to diagonally opposed corners of the
   square frame. Dip the entire frame into the soap solution.
   Carefully raise the frame out of the solution, and observe the
   behavior of the thread. Make a sketch and record your observations. Puncture the film on one side of the thread with a
   clean toothpick, and observe what happens to the thread.
   Sketch what you see as accurately as possible. Repeat, punc-
   turing alternate sides of the film.
B. Slide one end of the thread to a different corner of the frame,
   and repeat Procedure A. Record your observations.

Herb Comess

Figure 2 · 17.
Carrying out
Procedure D.

C. Dip the U-frame (and sliding bar) into the soap solution, and remove. Gently grasp the sliding bar on both ends and pull it slowly toward the block. Predict what will happen when you release the bar. Release the sliding bar and observe the effect. Was your prediction correct? Record your observations.

D. Form a film on the large end of the glass funnel by gently dipping it into the soap solution. Cover the small end of the funnel with your finger, and raise the funnel from the solution. Before continuing, predict what will happen to the film when you remove your finger from the funnel. Hold the funnel at eye level as shown in Figure 2·17 on page 36 and remove your finger. Observe and record in your notebook any change in the film.

E. Repeat the steps of Procedure D, and then dip the funnel into the soap solution to form a second film. Record your observations carefully.

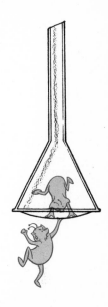

Figure 2·18. A possible explanation for the behavior of films in Procedures D and E.

INTERPRETATIONS

1. Combining your observations from Investigation 2 and 3, write a description of a model that relates the behavior of water to the particles which join together to make water drops. In giving reasons for your statements, you are carrying out a fundamental activity of science: the relating of experimental results and the interpretation of those results in such a way as either to build more confidence in the model or to provide evidence that makes the model unsatisfactory.

2. As in Investigation 2, the following questions should serve only as guidelines, not as restrictions on your thinking:

   a. In Procedures A and B you punctured one-half of the film. What does the behavior of the thread following a puncture suggest about the properties of atoms or the behavior of demons?

   b. How can you account for the behavior of the film in Procedure C? How can you account for the reaction of the soap film and sliding bar after it is released?

   c. Why does a film formed on the large end of a funnel behave as it does?

Figure 2 · 19.
This insect can
walk on water.
What keeps the
insect from
sinking?

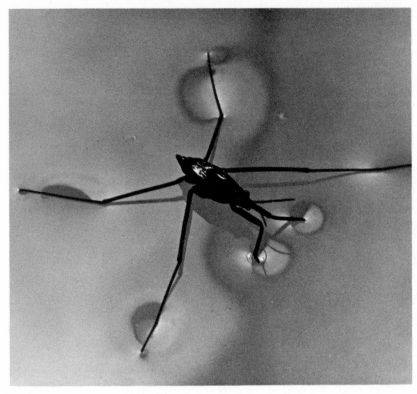

John Seginski

Components of Matter

The chalk particles used in Investigation 1 all resemble one another, except for size and shape. They all have the same color and texture. If you could continue breaking the chalk particles apart, do you think there would be one kind of particle, or might there be several kinds? What holds the particles together? If you were able to break the particles into atoms, would all the atoms behave the same way?

The composition of chalk cannot be changed by simple mechanical means, such as crushing. Chemical experiments show that chalk is made from a combination of three different substances. When chalk is heated to 800° C. (1472° F.), it gives off a gas. The properties of the white, solid substance that remains are quite different from those of chalk. The new substance is called lime (used in making mortar). When lime is heated to 2572° C. it melts. If an electric current is then passed through it, the molten lime will decompose into calcium metal and oxygen gas. Try as you may, you cannot separate these last two substances into any other materials.

INTERPRETATIONS

1. From the preceding discussion it is possible to make some interpretations about the characteristics and properties of atoms and chalk. List as many interpretations as you can.
2. A gas is given off when chalk is heated to a high temperature. What experimental procedures might you use to determine whether this gas is a substance that can be broken apart or a substance (such as calcium or oxygen) that cannot be broken apart?
3. If chalk is made up of atoms, something must hold them together. Assume that demons are responsible, and try to state some of the laws that must govern their behavior.

Breaking down chalk in the way just described would be very difficult. So that you may gain some experience in separating matter, materials that are easier to work with have been selected for the next investigation. When you look at a sample of matter, it may not be possible to tell if it can be broken apart, but if substances are chemically different, it is possible to use their differences in behavior to separate them.

INVESTIGATION 4: Separating Components of Matter

MATERIALS (per team)
Strip of filter paper with dye spot
Paper clip
2 Mason jars or drinking glasses

PROCEDURES

A. Pour about 20 ml of water into one of the jars. A spot of green dye has been placed near one end of the filter paper. Hold the filter paper against the *outside* of the jar so the dye spot is a short distance above the water level. Push a straightened paper clip through the filter paper at the level even with the top of the jar.

B. Lower the filter paper into the water until the clip rests on the jar (Figure 2 · 20).

Figure 2 · 20.
Set-up for
Procedures A–D.

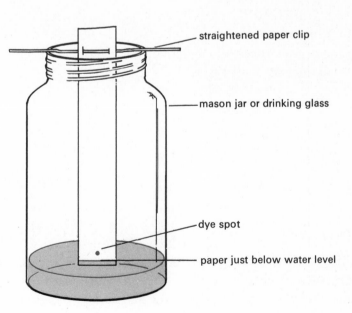

straightened paper clip

mason jar or drinking glass

dye spot

paper just below water level

C. Leave the filter paper in the water until the paper is saturated to the level of the paper clip.

D. Remove the filter paper from the water and hang it in an empty jar to dry. Do not touch the paper.

INTERPRETATIONS

1. How many substances were present in the original dye?
2. What property of matter do you believe is responsible for the separation?
3. Suggest a model to explain how the separation could occur. You might suggest demons or some other theory to explain why the substances in the dye separated. Make your own illustrations, if necessary.

An End and a Beginning

The presence of demons could be used to explain what you have observed about the behavior of matter. Investigations in Section Two also provided evidence that matter may be composed of many small particles. This information can be used to develop a theory to explain the behavior of matter. The idea that matter is made up of small particles, called atoms and molecules, and that the behavior of any substance depends on the properties of these particles is called the atomic-molecular theory of matter.

The investigations in Section Two do not *prove* that the atomic-molecular theory is true, but they do provide substantial evidence for the existence of atoms and molecules. Scientists are continually seeking new evidence to support this theory of matter.

The world of atoms can be as challenging to explore as outer space. Scientists continue their search for knowledge about atoms as well as about planets. If the present rate of scientific advance continues, knowledge about our environment will probably double within the next ten years. What changes this knowledge will bring cannot be known, but we can be sure that life will be different.

By investigating, observing, interpreting, and communicating, scientists throughout the world have developed a model that helps to explain, as well as predict, the behavior of matter. This model has been developed partly from experiments that required complicated equipment and advanced knowledge. But it also has been constructed from investigations quite similar to those you will perform in the following sections of this course.

REFERENCES

Born, Max. *The Restless Universe.* New York: Dover Publications, Inc., 1951.

Boys, C. C. *Soap Bubbles and the Forces Which Mold Them.* Garden City, N.Y.: Doubleday & Co., Inc. (Anchor Books), 1959.

DeVries, Leonard. *The Book of the Atom.* New York: The Macmillan Co., 1960.

Lapp, Ralph E. and the Editors of *Life. Matter.* New York: Time Inc. (Time-Life Books), 1965.

Classification of the Elements: The Structure of Atoms

You have made some of the same observations and performed some of the same kinds of investigations that led scientists to construct a model for the behavior and structure of matter. You have observed that the smallest particles of matter must be too small to see. And like Democritus, you have used the term *atoms* as a name for these particles.

As you have seen, matter can be separated into different kinds of substances. Therefore, there must be different kinds of atoms. Scientists recognized the need to classify them into groups. After atoms are grouped, their properties may be studied more easily. Biologists do the same thing when they classify different kinds of trees—oaks, pines, willows, and so forth. Geologists classify the different minerals, and astronomers place stars, planets, moons, and meteors in separate groups. Classification—the grouping of things in an orderly manner—is an important and useful part of science.

According to our present atomic theory, all the substances familiar to us are made up of atoms of elements. An *element* is a substance that cannot be separated by chemical means into anything other than a sample of that substance. For example, we say that gold is an element because the smallest particle of gold

Figure 3 · 1.
Symbols for gold
that have been
used in the past.
Why do you
think modern
scientists use Au
as a symbol
for gold?

fifteenth century

sixteenth century

1783 (Bergman)

1808 (Dalton)

1814 (Berzalius)

Figure 3 · 2.
Symbols and
descriptions for
eighteen com-
mon elements.

dust still has the properties of gold.

An *atom* is the smallest possible unit of an element. An atom of gold is the smallest possible particle of gold.

Gradually scientists began to use a set of symbols—one for each element. Symbols are used for convenience, and very often they contain clues to what they represent. The modern symbol for gold—Au—is taken from the Latin word *aurum*, meaning gold. Symbols for some of the elements have been used since the fifteenth century.

The system of element symbols now used throughout the world was introduced in 1814 by Jöns J. Berzelius, a Swedish chemist. Most symbols are initials or abbreviations of the Greek or Latin names for the elements. Since the names of several elements start with the same first letter, a second letter has been added to some of the symbols to avoid confusion. For example, the symbol for carbon is C; for calcium, Ca; for cesium, Cs. Symbols and pictures of some of the common elements are shown in Figure 3 · 2 and following color inserts.

Element	Symbol	Description
Aluminum	Al	Silvery metal
Argon	Ar	Colorless gas
Beryllium	Be	Silvery metal
Boron	B	Yellowish-brown crystal
Carbon	C	Black crystal
Chlorine	Cl	Greenish gas
Fluorine	F	Pale yellow gas
Helium	He	Colorless gas
Hydrogen	H	Colorless gas
Lithium	Li	Silvery metal
Magnesium	Mg	Silvery metal
Neon	Ne	Colorless gas
Nitrogen	N	Colorless gas
Oxygen	O	Colorless gas
Phosphorus	P	Red, white, or yellow crystal
Silicon	Si	Silvery gray crystal
Sodium	Na	Silvery metal
Sulfur	S	Yellow crystal

Figure 3 · 2. Color photographs of some of the elements shown
in the table on page 44.

Aluminum.

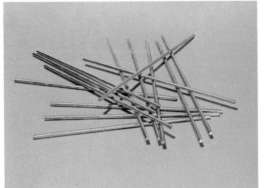

Herb Comess

Beryllium.

Herb Comess

Boron.

Herb Comess

Carbon.

Herb Comess

Chlorine. Neil L. Hill for Argonne National Laboratory

Fluorine. Neil L. Hill for Argonne National Laboratory

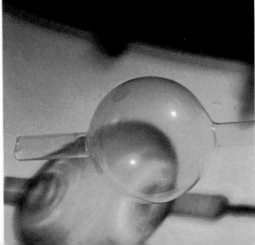

Lithium, photographed in kerosene.

Phosphorous (yellow), photographed in water.

Sodium, photographed in kerosene.

Magnesium.

Silicon.

Sulfur.

Grouping Elements by Appearance

You are already familiar with a number of elements, such as gold, silver, iron, copper, and oxygen. Your first problem in Section Three is to find a way to arrange the eighteen elements in logical groups based only on the information given in Figure 3 · 2.

Use any system you wish for grouping. After completing the problem, compare your system of grouping the elements with those used by other students.

INTERPRETATIONS

1. Describe the advantages of your method of grouping elements.
2. Describe what you believe to be the disadvantages of your method of grouping.
3. What are some advantages of using symbols for the elements?

Grouping Elements by Their Structure and Behavior

Grouping elements by appearance does not give us information about how they behave or react. Sugar and salt may look alike. But you know they do not have the same taste. And under certain conditions the two behave in different ways.

Scientists use behavior as one means of classifying elements. To understand the advantages of this type of classification, you should first investigate some of the ways in which matter behaves.

INVESTIGATION 5: Observing Effects of Electrical Charges

Most people have noticed that a spark may be produced when certain materials are rubbed together. You may have heard the crackle of sparks while combing your hair or brushing your dog. You may have received a slight shock from touching a doorknob after walking across a rug. In this investigation you will study the effects of such electrical charges on the behavior of matter.

MATERIALS (per team)
 2 plastic rulers (6- or 12-inch)
 Ring stand and clamp (or other support)
 Thread
 2 small pieces of masking tape
 Piece of wool cloth (6 x 6 inches)
 Piece of plastic food wrap (8 x 8 inches)

PROCEDURES
A. Suspend a plastic ruler from the ring stand (Figure 3 · 3). Adjust the thread so the ruler will not touch any other object.
B. Rub both ends of the suspended ruler with wool cloth. Take care not to touch the ends after the ruler has been rubbed. Rub one end of the second ruler with wool and hold it about one inch from one end of the suspended ruler. Repeat, using the opposite end of the suspended ruler. Record your observations in your notebook.

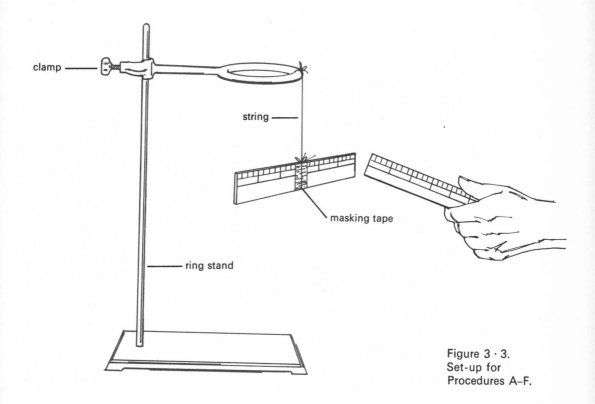

clamp

string

masking tape

ring stand

Figure 3 · 3.
Set-up for
Procedures A–F.

C. Repeat Procedure B, but rub *both* rulers with plastic wrap instead of wool cloth. Record your observations.

INTERPRETATIONS

1. How might you account for the behavior of the two rulers after they are rubbed with wool? with plastic wrap?

PROCEDURES (continued)

D. Rub both ends of the suspended ruler with wool. Rub one end of the second ruler with plastic wrap. Hold the second ruler about 1 inch from one end of the suspended ruler. Record your observations.

INTERPRETATIONS (continued)

2. In what way (if any) does the result of Procedure D affect your answer to Interpretation 1?

PROCEDURES (continued)

E. Repeat Procedure D, but hold the *plastic wrap* (not the ruler) near one end of the suspended ruler. Sketch and record the result in your notebook.

INTERPRETATIONS (continued)

3. Compare the result of Procedure D with that of Procedure E.

PROCEDURES (continued)

F. Before carrying out this procedure, read the directions and predict the result. Rub both ends of the suspended ruler with wool. Rub the second ruler with only one corner of the wool. Hold that corner (not the ruler) near one end of the suspended ruler.

INTERPRETATIONS (continued)

4. Were you able to correctly predict the result of Procedure F from the result of Procedure E?

PROBLEM

1. Construct a model to explain why plastic wrap and wool produce different effects on the rulers. Use the following questions in building your model.
    a. Rubbing certain materials together may create static electricity. Is there a relationship between static electricity and the behavior of rulers after they have been rubbed with wool or plastic wrap?
    b. If matter contains electricity, where do you think the electricity is located?
    c. In Section Two you were introduced to the idea of attraction between particles. Could this idea explain the results of Investigation 5? Could a demon theory account for the results of this investigation?

The Work of Rutherford

You have seen that the kind of electrical charge placed on two objects determines whether the objects will attract or repel each other. Early in this century, Ernest Rutherford (1871–1937) investigated the electrical properties of matter by studying certain radioactive elements. Atoms of these elements give off tiny *alpha* particles, which travel at extremely high speeds. Alpha particles produce little flashes of light when they strike a specially coated glass plate. This plate can be used as a screen to detect alpha particles.

Rutherford thought that he might learn more about the nature of atoms if he projected a beam of alpha particles toward a very thin layer of matter. Gold is a soft metal and can be pressed into very thin sheets (foil). Rutherford placed a sheet of gold foil between his detecting screen and a radioactive source. He saw many little flashes of light on the screen (see Figure 3 · 4 on the following page). Apparently the alpha particles had passed through the foil.

Rutherford and some of his students observed that most of the particles continued along almost straight paths after passing through the foil. But they also noticed that about one out of every ten thousand particles changed direction as it passed through the foil. The angle of change was often more than ten degrees. On rare occasions an alpha particle was reflected almost directly backward by the gold foil. This was a surprise. In Rutherford's own words, "It was about as incredible as if you had fired a 15-inch shell at a piece of tissue paper and it came back and hit you."

The following questions and statements are intended to help you understand Rutherford's work. Carefully study each one in order.

1. When two objects (such as two plastic rulers) have like charges, how do the objects affect each other?
2. As you bring two objects with like charges closer together, what happens to the strength of the effect the objects have on one another?
3. What happens when a charged ruler is held near a very small

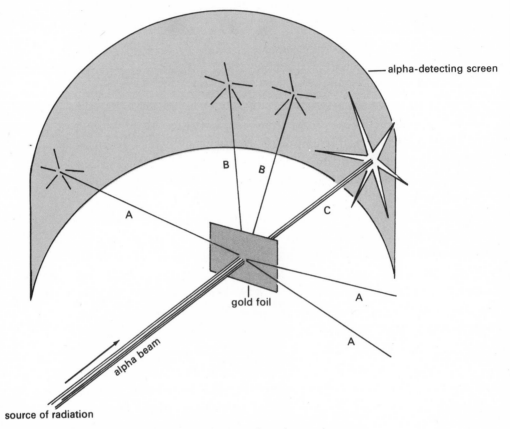

Figure 3 · 4. Diagram of the apparatus Rutherford used to detect the presence of alpha particles. Lines marked *A* represent the paths of reflected alpha particles. Lines marked *B* represent the paths of deflected particles. *C* represents alpha particles that did not change direction.

piece of paper? What happens if the same charged ruler is held near a much larger piece of paper?

4. When alpha particles pass through gold foil, only about one out of every ten thousand particles changes direction. Most of the changes in direction are slight. The direction taken by a few particles changes quite a bit. A very few even bounce back toward the source of radiation. Construct a model for the structure of gold foil that will help explain these observations.

5. Very few of the alpha particles are deflected by the gold foil.

But *none* of the gold atoms move. Construct (in your mind) a model of an atom of gold. The model should be as simple as possible; but be sure it is consistent with the observations. Describe your model of an atom of gold.

6. If a beam of negatively charged electrons strikes a piece of tin foil (or gold foil), the foil becomes negatively charged. If a beam of alpha particles strikes tin foil (or gold foil), the foil becomes positively charged. From this information, what kind of charge do you think an alpha particle has?

7. Explain how an atom of gold could be electrically neutral and still affect moving alpha particles.

Discovery of Particles

Early in the nineteenth century a new atomic theory for the structure of matter was proposed. Atoms were regarded as the basic building blocks of matter. They were thought to be indivisible and without internal structure. By the late 1800's and early 1900's, experiments showed that such a simple model cannot explain the behavior of matter. The existence of particles smaller than atoms was suggested.

The Electron

The *electron*, first of the particles to be discovered, is the lightest of the particles. All electrons have an equal, negative electrical charge.

Most of the volume of an atom is occupied by its electrons. *Only the electrons are transferred in chemical reactions.*

Hundreds of experiments, carried out by many men, were necessary to find out about the properties of electrons. Four men received the Nobel Prize for their experiments which greatly contributed to further understanding of electron theory. Philipp E. Lenard of Germany received the Nobel Prize in physics in 1905 for his study of the behavior of charged particles in air. Joseph J. Thomson of England was awarded the Nobel Prize in 1906 for his experiments on the behavior of electrons in a magnetic field. Robert A. Millikan of the United States received the Nobel Prize for physics in 1923 for measuring the charge on electrons. Jean B. Perrin of France was awarded the Nobel Prize in 1926 for his discoveries about the discontinuous structure of matter and for measuring the size of atoms.

The Proton

Next to be discovered was the *proton*. A proton is about 1836 times heavier than an electron. All protons have an equal, positive electrical charge. The simplest atom, hydrogen, has just one proton and one electron. An atom of hydrogen is electrically neutral because the proton's positive charge is equal to the electron's negative charge. Because the proton and the electron have opposite kinds of charge, they will attract each other and stay very close together.

The number of protons in an atom is the factor that makes one element different from another. Every atom of hydrogen has only one proton. There are ninety-two protons in every atom of the heaviest natural element, uranium. The following table shows the number of protons per atom for some of the more common elements.

Figure 3 · 5. Protons in the atoms of some common elements.

	Carbon	Nitrogen	Oxygen	Aluminum	Sulfur	Iron	Gold
Number of protons per atom	6	7	8	13	16	26	79

The number of protons in one atom of an element is the *atomic number* of that element. Each element has a different atomic number. An element has been identified for every atomic number up to 103. The elements with atomic numbers from 1 to 92 occur in nature. The other eleven have been made by man. Elements with more than 103 protons per atom will probably be produced in the future. But the higher the atomic number, the more difficult (and expensive) the element is to produce.

Ernest Rutherford's work with alpha particles showed that protons are not scattered throughout the atom, but are concentrated in a very small region called the *nucleus*.

The Neutron

In 1932, another kind of atomic particle was discovered—the *neutron* (for neutral particle). A neutron is just as heavy as a proton, but it is electrically neutral. The nuclei of all atoms except those of hydrogen are made up of tightly packed protons and neutrons. The nucleus of a hydrogen atom contains no neutrons and only 1 proton.

Atomic Weight

If we use 1 proton (or neutron) as a unit of weight, we can say that the sum of the number of protons and neutrons in an atom is equal to the weight of that atom. A hydrogen atom, for example, has only 1 proton, so its weight is 1. A helium atom, with 2 protons and 2 neutrons, has a weight of 4.

All atoms of an element must have the same number of protons, but the number of neutrons may vary. For this reason atoms of the same element may have different weights. A chemist deals with large numbers of atoms at a time. Therefore, he is not usually interested in the weight of any one atom—but in the average weight of atoms for each element. This average is called the *atomic weight of the element.*

Figure 3 · 6.
Summary of
atomic particles.

	Proton	Neutron	Electron
Comparative weight of particles	1	1	$\dfrac{1}{1836}$
Electric charge of one particle	+1	0	−1
Location	Nucleus	Nucleus	Outside the nucleus
Transferred in chemical change	No	No	Yes

PROBLEMS

1. Must all atoms of the same element have the same weight? Give reasons for your answer.
2. What is the weight and the atomic number of an atom having 4 protons and 5 neutrons?
3. An atom of sodium has 11 protons and a weight of 23. What is the atomic number of the sodium atom? How many neutrons does the sodium atom have?

Electrical Charge of Atoms

An atom must have an equal number of electrons and protons to be electrically neutral. For example, an atom of aluminum (atomic number 13) has 13 protons. To be neutral, it must also have 13 electrons. If some of the electrons are removed, the atom will have more protons than electrons. It will have a positive charge.

During Investigation 5 you may have observed that the plastic rulers did not remain permanently charged. They gradually became neutral. An atom may become negatively charged by gaining electrons. If this happens, the atom will then return to the neutral state by giving off the extra electrons to its surroundings. In Investigation 5 the wool lost electrons to the plastic ruler as a result of the physical process of rubbing. Then the plastic ruler gradually lost the extra electrons to its surroundings (perhaps to the air). The wool regained its lost electrons (perhaps from the air). Whenever a physical process (in this case, rubbing plastic and wool together) produces charges on two different objects, one object will be positively charged, the other negatively charged. If the two objects are brought together again in such a way that electrons can move from one to the other, the two objects will become neutral.

Experiments in which electrons are removed from neutral atoms yield valuable information. Three electrons can be removed from aluminum (atomic number 13) rather easily. However, removal of a fourth electron is very difficult. Only two electrons can be removed easily from magnesium (atomic number 12). If all electrons are removed, one at a time, from atoms of these elements, it becomes evident that there are three groups of electrons in each atom. In an aluminum atom the easiest group to remove contains 3 electrons. The next group contains 8 electrons. And the group most difficult to remove contains 2 electrons. From this information it is possible to construct a model of the aluminum atom.

Changing Models of Atomic Structure

Approximately forty years ago a relatively simple atomic model would have accounted for most of the facts then known about atoms. According to this model, electrons moved in definite orbits around the heavier nucleus.

Figure 3·7 and 3·8 are planetary models of an aluminum atom, with the heavy nucleus (protons and neutrons) surrounded by orbiting electrons. The models show a total of 13 electrons distributed in three orbits: 2 electrons in the inner orbit, 8 in the middle orbit, and 3 in the outer orbit.

The planetary model of an atom was an attempt to explain the behavior of atoms in a simple way, by comparing their structures to the easily visualized (and accepted) structure of our solar system. It now appears that electrons do not follow fixed paths about

Figure 3·7. Planetary model of an aluminum atom. According to this model, the electrons travel in fixed paths.

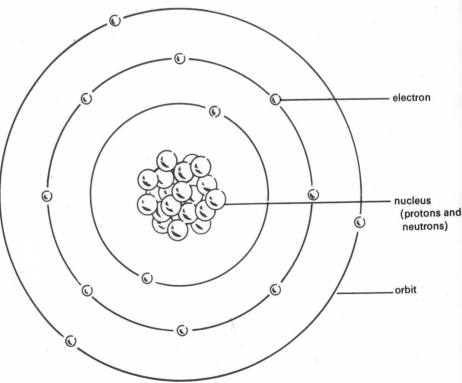

electron

nucleus (protons and neutrons)

orbit

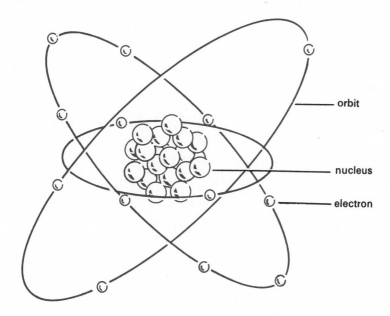

Figure 3 · 8. Three-dimensional model of an aluminum atom, in which the electrons orbit in different planes.

orbit

nucleus

electron

the nucleus. Many kinds of chemical activity could be explained by using this planetary model. But some reactions did *not* fit the model, so changes were necessary.

It is not our intention to make a complete study of the most modern and complex atomic model. Instead, a simplified version of an atomic model may help you to understand some of the basic principles of chemical activity. This model is somewhat more useful, yet no more complex, than the planetary model.

Figures 3 · 9 and 3 · 10 on page 58 show models of the same kind of atom. The grouping of electrons is similar in the two models. But the electron cloud model does not show specific electron paths, or orbits, around the nucleus. Instead, the groups of electrons are pictured as clouds of negative charge. The electrons do not orbit around the nucleus on fixed paths. They occur in several distinct regions, and they are held in the regions by the attraction of the nucleus. The larger the region occupied by the electrons, the easier they are to remove from the atoms. Thus the three electrons in an aluminum atom's outer cloud are more easily removed by chemical activity than are electrons in the two smaller clouds.

region of 3 electrons ——————————————

region of 8 electrons ——————————————

region of 2 electrons ——————————————

nucleus ——————————————

Figure 3 · 9.
Electron-cloud
model of an
aluminum atom.

Figure 3 · 10.
Simplified model
of an aluminum
atom.

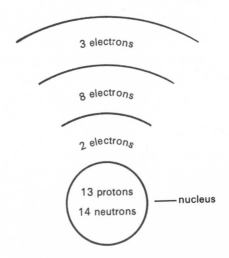

3 electrons

8 electrons

2 electrons

13 protons
14 neutrons

——— nucleus

For convenience we may illustrate this model in a simpler form, as in Figure 3·10.

When a transfer of electrical charge results from a physical process, there must be a source of energy. In Investigation 5 *you* were the source of energy that produced the separation of charge. You started with two neutral objects and rubbed them together. When you finished, one was negative and the other was positive. A chemical reaction also involves a rearrangement of charge. Some chemical reactions do not require an outside source of energy. Others require a small amount of energy to start and then produce a great deal of energy as they continue. The combining of iron and oxygen to produce rust is a familiar example of a reaction that needs no outside source of energy to begin. A small amount of energy is required to start a fire. The fire then releases a great deal of energy until all the fuel is used up. Surely all of the heat and light from a campfire is not stored in the match that starts it!

To help you understand how chemical reactions occur, we might divide elements into two categories—metals and nonmetals. Atoms of some elements hold their electrons very tightly, while others do not. Nonmetals hold onto electrons tightly. Sulfur and iodine are examples of nonmetals.

Atoms of metals have only a weak attraction for their outer electrons. Aluminum and copper are common elements classified as metals.

A basic difference between metals and nonmetals seems to be that electrons can be removed rather easily from metals, while nonmetals tend to gain and keep electrons.

A large number of chemical reactions involve the combination of a metal and a nonmetal.

INVESTIGATION 6: Charged Particles in Solution

Investigation 5 provided evidence that electrons can be added to or removed from some objects. The transfer of electrons results in these objects becoming either positively or negatively charged. If two objects have unlike charges, the objects will attract each other. If the charges are the same, the objects will repel each other.

During this investigation you will study the effect of electricity on particles in solution.

MATERIALS (per team)
  2 paper clips
  2 lengths of bell wire (10-inch)
  250-ml beaker
  150 ml of distilled water
  12-inch length of dialysis tubing
  6-volt battery
  10 ml of iodine-potassium iodide solution (IKI)

Figure 3 · 11.
Set-up for
Procedures A–D.

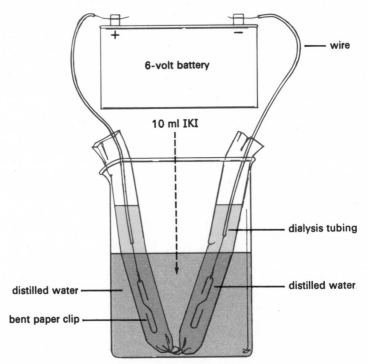

PROCEDURES

Set up the apparatus shown in Figure 3 · 11 as follows:

A. Unfold two paper clips so their lengths are doubled. Remove the insulation from the ends of both bell wires. Fasten a wire to one end of each unfolded paper clip.

B. Half-fill a beaker with distilled water. Moisten the dialysis tubing, and tie a knot in the middle of it. Hold up the ends of the tubing and fill each half with distilled water to a depth of about 4 inches. Carefully lower the dialysis tubing into the beaker of water and fold the free ends of the tubing over the edge. Insert a paper clip electrode into the water in each half of the tubing. Attach the free ends of the wires to the battery.

NOTE: Electricity from the battery will supply electrons to one paper clip and remove electrons from the other. Thus one paper clip will have excess electrons and be negatively charged, while the other will be positively charged.

C. Add 10 ml of the brown-colored (IKI) solution to the water in the beaker. Allow the paper clips to remain connected to the battery for about twenty minutes.

D. Mark or label each end of the tubing with a + (positive) or − (negative) sign to match the poles on the battery. Disconnect the battery and remove the electrodes from the tubing. Lift the tubing out of the beaker and observe any changes that may have occurred in each half.

INTERPRETATIONS

1. What happened to the water in the tubing that was connected to the positive side of the battery? What happened on the negative side?

2. Do you think that particles of the brown-colored solution have a positive charge or a negative charge?

3. From the results of this investigation, what evidence do you have that
    a. neutral atoms might lose electrons and become positively charged?
    b. neutral atoms might gain electrons and become negatively charged?

REFERENCES

Andrade, Edward. *Rutherford and the Nature of the Atom.* ("Science Study Series") Garden City, N.Y.: Doubleday & Co., Inc. (Anchor Books), 1964.

Asimov, Isaac. *Breakthroughs in Science.* Boston: Houghton Mifflin Co., 1959.

DeVries, Leonard. *The Book of the Atom.* New York: The Macmillan Co., 1960.

Ford, Kenneth W. *The World of Elementary Particles.* New York: Blaisdell Publishing Co., 1963.

Gamow, George. *Matter, Earth, & Sky.* Englewood Cliffs, N.J.: Prentice-Hall, 1958.

Haber, Heinz. *Our Friend the Atom.* New York: Simon & Schuster, 1956.

Hughes, Donald J. *Neutron Story.* ("Science Study Series") Garden City, N.Y.: Doubleday & Co., Inc. (Anchor Books), 1959.

Posin, Daniel Q. *What Is Matter.* Chicago: Benefic Press, 1962.

Rueben, Gabriel H., and Di Stefano, Joseph. *What Is An Atom?* Chicago: Benefic Press, 1960.

Classification of the Elements: Refining a Model

When two or more elements *react* (combine) they produce a new substance called a compound. In every compound the atoms are bonded (joined together) in a certain way. A molecule of water (formula H_2O) is made up of two atoms of hydrogen joined to one atom of oxygen. There are hundreds of thousands of different compounds, each with its own particular combination of elements. Sugar is made from the elements carbon, hydrogen, and oxygen. Table salt is made from sodium and chlorine.

Experiments during the last one hundred and fifty years have provided evidence that elements can be organized into groups according to behavior. Investigations like those you have performed, the work of Rutherford, and many other experiments have been used as evidence that the numbers of protons or electrons in atoms might be the key to classifying elements into groups.

In Section Three you saw evidence that chemical reactions involve the transfer of electrical charge. According to your model of an atom—a small positive nucleus surrounded by electrons—the transfer of electric charge is a transfer of electrons from one atom to another. Some atoms tend to lose electrons, while other atoms tend to attract and keep electrons.

Your next problem will be to group elements according to their ability to gain or lose electrons. In this way you may be able to predict which elements should combine to form compounds.

Figure 4 · 1.
Properties of
some elements.

Element	Symbol	Description	Atomic Number	Number of Electrons Readily Gained or Lost
Aluminum	Al	silvery metal	13	3 lost
Argon	Ar	colorless gas	18	0 lost or gained
Beryllium	Be	silvery metal	4	2 lost
Boron	B	yellowish-brown crystal	5	3 lost
Carbon	C	black crystal	6	4 lost or gained
Chlorine	Cl	yellow-green gas	17	1 gained
Fluorine	F	pale-yellow gas	9	1 gained
Helium	He	colorless gas	2	0 lost or gained
Hydrogen	H	colorless gas	1	1 lost
Lithium	Li	silvery metal	3	1 lost
Magnesium	Mg	silvery metal	12	2 lost
Neon	Ne	colorless gas	10	0 lost or gained
Nitrogen	N	colorless gas	7	3 gained
Oxygen	O	colorless gas	8	2 gained
Phosphorus	P	red or yellow crystal	15	3 gained
Silicon	Si	silvery crystal	14	4 lost or gained
Sodium	Na	silvery metal	11	1 lost
Sulphur	S	yellow crystal	16	2 gained

PROBLEMS

1. Examine Figure 4 · 1 carefully. It is similar to Figure 3 · 2, but it contains additional information. To organize this data, prepare a chart in your notebook like the one shown in Figure 4 · 2. List the elements from left to right, in order of increasing atomic number. For each element be sure to include the sym-

bol, the atomic number (number of protons), and the number of electrons gained or lost. The data for hydrogen is provided as an example.

Figure 4 · 2.

Electrons Gained or Lost	1 L															
Element	H															
Atomic Number	1															

2. Study your completed chart carefully. What pattern do you see in the numbers of electrons gained or lost?

3. Prepare a new chart that groups the elements according to the number of electrons gained or lost and also keeps them in order of atomic number. Start a new row each time the pattern you observed in Problem 2 is repeated. Your new chart should contain several rows of elements instead of one.

INTERPRETATIONS

1. Suggest at least one compound that could result from a transfer of electrons.

2. Which element would not be likely to combine with anything?

3. Compare the chart you prepared in Problem 3 with your method of grouping elements in the problem on page 45. Which way of arranging elements is more useful—according to appearance or according to atomic number? Why?

Groups of Elements

There are many useful ways to group elements. The local power company might prefer to group elements according to the ease with which they conduct electricity. The jeweler might want to classify elements according to their ability to resist corrosion. The chemist is interested in the way in which elements combine to form compounds. Groups of elements that exhibit similar behavior when combined with other elements are called *families* of elements. A brief discussion of a few of these families follows.

The Helium Family

With few exceptions, the six gases in the helium family (Figure 4·3) are not involved in chemical reactions. They are therefore called *inert* (unchanging) gases. The members of this family are grouped together because they generally lack the ability to combine among themselves or with elements of other families. Although it is more expensive to produce than hydrogen, helium is used in blimps because it is not explosive. (Hydrogen was used in the famous German dirigible *Hindenberg*, which exploded and burned in 1937.) Neon is commonly used in advertising signs.

With the exception of radon, the members of the helium family were discovered within the four-year period from 1894 to 1898. Members of this family do not tend to react chemically. They are gases present in very small amounts in air, and their discovery depended upon finding some means of isolating them. After it became possible to compress air under great pressure—forming liquid air—these elements were discovered. Elements of the helium family remain after the oxygen and nitrogen in liquid air are boiled away.

Since the nucleus of an atom is not directly involved in chemical reactions, the lack of chemical reactivity of the inert gases probably has something to do with the structure of their electron groups. The behavior of members of other chemical families will be a test of this hypothesis.

Name	Symbol	Atomic Number	Atomic Weight	Number of Electrons Per Group					
Helium	He	2	4.0	2					
Neon	Ne	10	20.2	2	8				
Argon	Ar	18	39.9	2	8	8			
Krypton	Kr	36	83.8	2	8	18	8		
Xenon	Xe	54	131.3	2	8	18	18	8	
Radon	Rn	86	222.0	2	8	18	32	18	8

Figure 4 · 3. The helium family.

The Fluorine (or Halogen) Family

Unlike the inert gases, fluorine and other members of this family (Figure 4·4) combine readily with many other elements. Though these four elements are similar in their chemical reactions, they differ considerably in physical appearance. At room temperature fluorine and chlorine are gases, bromine is a liquid, and iodine is a solid. Members of this family range in color from pale green to purplish gray. Solutions of iodine are used as antiseptics. Chlorine is used to purify water. Some compounds of fluorine are apparently effective in preventing tooth decay.

Name	Symbol	Atomic Number	Atomic Weight	Number of Electrons Per Group				
Fluorine	F	9	19.0	2	7			
Chlorine	Cl	17	35.5	2	8	7		
Bromine	Br	35	79.9	2	8	18	7	
Iodine	I	53	126.9	2	8	18	18	7

Figure 4 · 4. The fluorine (or halogen) family.

The Oxygen Family

Oxygen is a colorless gas; sulfur is a bright yellow solid. All other members of this family are silver-gray solids.

Notice that each atom of an element in this family (see Figure 4·5 on the following page) has 6 electrons in its outer group. Scientists think that chemical activity depends on the number of electrons in the outer group. As a result, the elements in the oxy-

Figure 4 · 5. The oxygen family.

Name	Symbol	Atomic Number	Atomic Weight	Number of Electrons Per Group					
Oxygen	O	8	16.0	2	6				
Sulfur	S	16	32.1	2	8	6			
Selenium	Se	34	79.0	2	8	18	6		
Tellurium	Te	52	127.6	2	8	18	18	6	
Polonium	Po	84	210.0	2	8	18	32	18	6

gen family react with hydrogen to produce compounds with similar *formulas*. Chemical formulas are made up of element symbols and numbers that show the quantity of atoms of each element present.

The following are formulas for compounds produced when members of the oxygen family react with hydrogen: H_2O, H_2S, H_2Se, H_2Te, and H_2Po. Though these compounds have similar formulas, they have very different properties (Figure 4 · 6). H_2O (water) is a substance necessary for life; but the hydrogen compounds formed by other members of the oxygen family are highly poisonous.

Figure 4 · 6. Examples of oxygen family members combined with hydrogen. In what way are the formulas for these compounds similar?

	Hydrogen Oxide (Water)	Hydrogen Sulfide	Hydrogen Selenide	Hydrogen Telluride
Formula	H_2O	H_2S	H_2Se	H_2Te
Odor	None	Rotten Eggs	Sour Garlic	Awful
Toxicity	None	Poisonous	Poisonous	Poisonous

The Nitrogen Family

Each atom of elements in this family has 5 electrons in its outer region (Figure 4 · 7).

Compounds containing nitrogen or phosphorus are found in all living cells. Many compounds containing arsenic have been used as insecticides and weed killers. Antimony and bismuth are metals; they are often mixed with copper to change its hardness or color.

Name	Symbol	Atomic Number	Atomic Weight	Number of Electrons Per Group					
Nitrogen	N	7	14.0	2	5				
Phosphorus	P	15	31.0	2	8	5			
Arsenic	As	33	74.9	2	8	18	5		
Antimony	Sb	51	121.8	2	8	18	18	5	
Bismuth	Bi	83	209.0	2	8	18	32	18	5

Figure 4 · 7. The nitrogen family.

The Carbon Family

Each atom of elements in this family has an outer group of 4 electrons (Figure 4 · 8). Because these elements tend either to gain or to lose 4 electrons, there is great variability among them.

Like nitrogen and phosphorus, carbon is found in all living things. It can form over a hundred thousand different compounds. For example, most of the material that makes up the paper in this book is a compound of carbon. Sugar, fats, gasoline, cotton, wool, and plastics are all compounds of carbon. Pure carbon may be black, as it is in soot, or it may form very hard crystals known as diamonds.

Name	Symbol	Atomic Number	Atomic Weight	Number of Electrons Per Group					
Carbon	C	6	12.0	2	4				
Silicon	Si	14	28.1	2	8	4			
Germanium	Ge	32	72.6	2	8	18	4		
Tin	Sn	50	118.7	2	8	18	18	4	
Lead	Pb	82	207.2	2	8	18	32	18	4

Figure 4 · 8. The carbon family.

Silicon is the most abundant element in the earth's crust. Many kinds of sand are compounds of silicon and oxygen. Ordinary garden soil includes many different silicon compounds.

Tin and lead are common metals, but pencil "lead" is a mixture of carbon and clay.

The Boron Family

There are 3 electrons in the outer group of an atom of each element in the boron family (Figure 4·9). Boron and aluminum commonly occur in mineral deposits and have many household uses. Other members of the family are very rare.

Figure 4·9.
The boron
family.

Name	Symbol	Atomic Number	Atomic Weight	Number of Electrons Per Group					
Boron	B	5	10.8	2	3				
Aluminum	Al	13	27.0	2	8	3			
Gallium	Ga	31	69.7	2	8	18	3		
Indium	In	49	114.8	2	8	18	18	3	
Thallium	T	81	204.4	2	8	18	32	18	3

You may have heard of borax and boric acid. Borax is a compound of boron, sodium, and oxygen and is often used as a cleaning and deodorizing agent. Boric acid contains boron, hydrogen, and oxygen and is sometimes used as an eyewash.

What would our lives be like without aluminum? Its lightness, strength, and low cost make modern air transportation possible. It is an excellent conductor of electricity, and many power transmission lines are made of aluminum. You may be familiar with its many uses in the home.

Gallium and indium are quite rare, but they are useful in some kinds of materials needed in the transistor industry.

Compounds of thallium have been used in poisons for controlling rodents.

The Beryllium Family (Alkaline Earths)

Each atom of an element in this family (Figure 4·10) has 2 electrons in its outer region. These electrons are easily lost to elements that gain electrons. Magnesium and calcium are present in many compounds found in the earth's crust. And both are present in living cells. Limestone is a combination of compounds of calcium, carbon, and oxygen.

Name	Symbol	Atomic Number	Atomic Weight	Number of Electrons Per Group						
Beryllium	Be	4	9.1	2	2					
Magnesium	Mg	12	24.3	2	8	2				
Calcium	Ca	20	40.1	2	8	8	2			
Strontium	Sr	38	87.6	2	8	18	8	2		
Barium	Ba	56	137.4	2	8	18	18	8	2	
Radium	Ra	88	226.0	2	8	18	32	18	8	2

Figure 4 · 10. The beryllium family (alkaline earths).

In pure form all elements in the beryllium family are metallic in appearance.

The Lithium Family

The most common elements in the lithium family (Figure 4 · 11) are sodium and potassium. Compounds of sodium and potassium are found in all living cells.

Each atom of an element in this family has only one electron in its outer group. Since this electron is easily removed, these elements are among the most reactive known. In chemical laborato-

Name	Symbol	Atomic Number	Atomic Weight	Number of Electrons Per Group						
Lithium	Li	3	6.9	2	1					
Sodium	Na	11	23.0	2	8	1				
Potassium	K	19	39.1	2	8	8	1			
Rubidium	Rb	37	85.5	2	8	18	8	1		
Cesium	Cs	55	132.9	2	8	18	18	8	1	
Francium	Fr	87	223.0	2	8	18	32	18	8	1

Figure 4 · 11. The lithium family.

ries, pure sodium and potassium are kept in kerosene to prevent them from reacting with oxygen or water in air. In pure form elements of this family look like typical metals, though they are somewhat softer than the metals used for construction purposes.

PROBLEMS FOR PRACTICE

Gases such as helium, neon, and argon, which belong to the helium family, usually do not react (combine) with each other or with other elements. Scientists believe that the electron groupings in atoms of these inert gases offer an explanation for this lack of reactivity. Scientists also believe that the reactivity of other elements depends upon the ease with which their atoms gain or lose electrons and achieve electron groupings like those of the inert gases.

Work each of the following problems to see how different elements may combine to form compounds.

1. Examine Figure 4 · 10 (the beryllium family). How might the electron grouping of calcium be changed to resemble the electron grouping of argon (Figure 4 · 3)?
2. Examine Figure 4 · 5 (the oxygen family). How might an atom of sulfur gain an electron grouping like that of argon?
3. Calcium and sulfur combine to form the compound calcium sulfide (CaS). Review the answers to Problems 1 and 2 and explain how the combination of calcium and sulfur results in an electron grouping like that of an inert gas for each element.
4. What is the electrical charge of a calcium atom? of a sulfur atom?
5. What would be the electrical charge of calcium after it lost 2 electrons? of sulfur after it gained 2 electrons?

ANSWERS TO PRACTICE PROBLEMS

1. Calcium has 2 electrons in its outer region. If it lost these 2 electrons its (new) outer region would have 8 electrons. Calcium would then have the same electron grouping as that of argon.
2. An atom of sulfur has 6 electrons in its outer region. If it gained 2 electrons, its outer region would have 8 electrons. Sulfur would then have the same electron grouping as argon.
3. In this reaction, calcium loses 2 electrons to sulfur. Both then have an electron grouping like argon, an inert gas.
4. A calcium atom has 20 protons (positive charge) and 20 electrons (negative charge). It is electrically neutral (zero

charge). Sulfur has 16 protons and 16 electrons and is also electrically neutral. (Check this by examining Figures 4·5 and 4·10.)

5. Calcium would have an electrical charge of +2, and sulfur would have a charge of −2.

PROBLEMS

Members of the helium family (with rare exceptions) are not able to combine chemically with other elements. Chemists believe that this lack of reactivity has something to do with the structure of their electron grouping.

1. How could a sodium atom acquire an electron grouping like that of neon?

2. How could a chlorine atom acquire an electron grouping like that of neon? like that of argon?

3. If an atom of sodium and an atom of chlorine are brought together, how might both atoms achieve an electron grouping like that of an inert gas?

4. How would this change affect the electrical balance (net charge) of each atom?

5. Using symbols, write formulas for the compounds most likely to be produced from a reaction between the following pairs of elements.[1]
   a. lithium and iodine
   b. sodium and bromine
   c. potassium and chlorine
   d. rubidium and fluorine
   e. cesium and bromine

6. What would have to happen to an atom of oxygen to give it an electron grouping like that of neon?

7. How many atoms of each of the following elements would be needed to supply the electron requirements of one oxygen atom?

---

[1]By general agreement among chemists, the symbol for the element that *loses* electrons is written first in a formula for a compound. For example, the formula for a compound of lithium and bromine is LiBr.

   a. sodium
   b. cesium
   c. magnesium
   d. barium

8. Frequently (as in Problem 7), chemical reactions require unequal numbers of atoms from the combining elements. In written formulas for such combinations, the number of atoms included from each element appears slightly below and to the right of each element's symbol. Where only one atom is included, no number is written. For example, you probably know that the formula for water is H_2O. The number 2 slightly below and to the right of H and the absence of any number after the O indicates that a molecule of water is formed from 2 atoms of hydrogen and one atom of oxygen. Now look at a more complex example: The formula for an aluminum oxide molecule is Al_2O_3; this means that the combining ratio for aluminum oxide is two atoms of aluminum (Al) to three atoms of oxygen. Now write the formula for the combination of oxygen with each element listed in Problem 7.

9. The atomic number of the element hydrogen is 1, and its atomic weight is 1.008.
   a. An atom of hydrogen has how many protons? how many neutrons? how many electrons?
   b. From its electron arrangement, to which family might hydrogen belong?
   c. What would be the formula for a combination of hydrogen and chlorine? of lithium and hydrogen? of calcium and hydrogen?

The Work of Mendeléeff

By 1830, fifty-five elements had been discovered. Each had different chemical properties, but no one had classified them according to these properties.

In 1864, the English chemist John Newlands arranged the elements known to him in order of their increasing atomic weights. He found that when the elements were arranged in vertical columns of seven, the horizontal rows contained elements which often have similar properties. There were so many exceptions to this, however, that other chemists thought little of his system.

A few years later, in 1869, the Russian chemist Dmitri Ivanovich Mendeléeff published a similar table, but one that avoided most of the difficulties of Newlands' arrangement. Mendeléeff took into account the "combining power" of elements (similar to the ability to gain or lose electrons) in addition to their atomic weights. He had so much confidence in his table that he left blank spaces in it when he could not find elements to fit the arrangement. He even predicted the discovery of elements to fit the blank spaces, and he described the properties of the unknown substances. His prediction turned out to be a good one, for within the next fifteen years elements possessing the predicted properties were discovered. Gallium (atomic weight 69.7) was isolated in 1875. Germanium (atomic weight 72.6) was isolated in 1886.

In his chart (Figure 4 · 12 on page 76) Mendeléeff listed the elements in vertical columns in order of increasing atomic weight. Where necessary, he started new columns so that elements with similar chemical properties would appear in the same horizontal row.

Because new discoveries are constantly being made in every field of scientific research, it is not surprising that there have been many changes in the organization of the Periodic Chart since the time of Mendeléeff.

Figure 4 · 12.
A portion of
Mendeléeff's
chart of the ele-
ments. Note that
he inserted ques-
tion marks to
indicate his belief
in the existence
of elements with
atomic weights
of 68 and 70—
even though
such elements
were unknown
in his time.

H=1			
	Be=9.4	Mg=24	Zn=65.2
	B=11	Al=27.4	?=68
	C=12	Si=28	?=70
	N=14	P=31	As=75
	O=16	S=32	Se=79.4
	F=19	Cl=35.5	Br=80
Li=7	Na=23	K=39	Rb=85.4
		Ca=40	Sr=87.6

PROBLEMS

1. Compare the horizontal rows of elements on Mendeléeff's chart with the charts of families of elements shown elsewhere in this section. In what ways are they different?

2. Why do you think Mendeléeff grouped elements into families differently than we do?

The Periodic Table of Elements

In science, as in any other field of study, it is desirable to organize information in ways that will make it useful. The information in Figures 4 · 3 through 4 · 11 is more convenient for study and comparison than written paragraphs containing the same information. Figure 4 · 13 goes one step further by combining the families in one table. This makes comparisons of families easier and gives us a basis for predicting formulas of compounds and reactivity of elements. The table is a modification of Mendeléeff's chart.

In the modern Periodic Table, elements are arranged in order of increasing atomic number and grouped according to similar chemical properties. The table of elements shown in Figure 4 · 13 includes only the families you have studied. It is not as complete as the one used by professional chemists and physicists. Study this modified table carefully.

PROBLEMS

1. The element astatine (At), a member of the fluorine family, has been intentionally omitted from the Periodic Table.
   a. What is its atomic number?
   b. What is the electron grouping for that atomic number?
2. a. Compare the electron groupings of hydrogen, lithium, beryllium, boron, and carbon with that of helium.
   b. Compare the electron groupings of carbon, nitrogen, oxygen, and fluorine with the electron grouping of neon.
3. The elements in some families tend to lose electrons. Elements in others tend to gain them. Carefully consider your answers to Problem 2. Make two lists—one of families that tend to gain electrons and another of families that tend to lose electrons.
4. a. Which family is made up of elements with the strongest tendency to lose electrons? Why?
   b. Which family is made up of elements with the strongest tendency to gain electrons? Why?
   c. Which family besides the inert gas family is made up of elements with the least tendency to gain *or* lose electrons? Why?

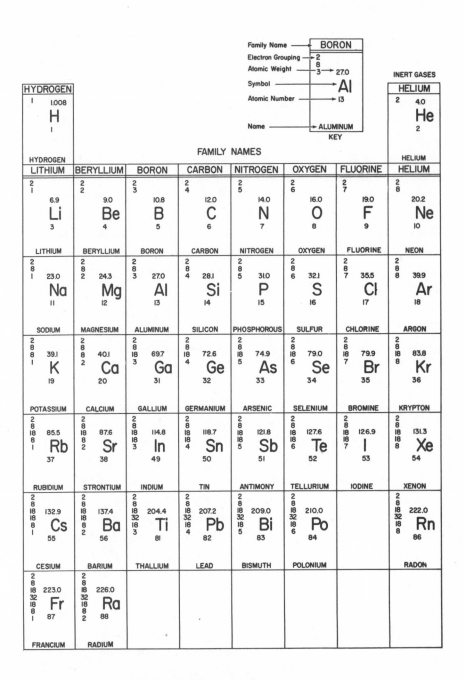

Figure 4 · 13. Partial periodic table of the elements.

The "Mole" Concept (Optional)

You know that atoms and molecules are very small—too small to be weighed one at a time. In fact, the most sensitive scale or balance cannot detect the difference in weight between 100,000 atoms and 500 billion atoms!

A larger, measurable, more workable unit must be established when an individual unit is too small to be conveniently detected or weighed. This unit must be made up of a certain number of the smaller units taken as a group.

Atoms and molecules are much too small to be seen or handled individually, so a larger unit—called a *mole*—is used. Atoms of hydrogen are lighter than atoms of any other kind of element. Chemists decided that one gram of hydrogen should be the standard. The number of atoms of hydrogen in one gram of hydrogen is the number of atoms in a mole. Many experiments have been carried out to find the number of atoms in a mole. The details of these experiments involve concepts, measurements, and assumptions beyond the scope of this course. The investigations indicate that the number of atoms in a mole is approximately 602,400,000,000,000,000,000,000 (usually written 6.024×10^{23}). This number is called *Avogadro's Number*, honoring Italian chemist Amedio Avogadro (1776–1856), who first suggested a method of comparing the relative molecular weights of different gases.

By determining the weight of the amount of an element that will combine with 1 gram of hydrogen, it is possible to establish how much 1 mole of that element would weigh. For simplicity we will use 6×10^{23} to represent the number of atoms in a mole. If 1 gram of hydrogen contains 6×10^{23} atoms (1 mole) then each atom of hydrogen must weigh $\dfrac{1}{6 \times 10^{23}}$ grams. (This is the same as saying that if one pound of oranges contains 3 oranges then each orange must weigh ⅓ of a pound.) If 1 atom of helium weighs 4 times as much as an atom of hydrogen, then 6×10^{23} atoms (1 mole) of helium must weigh 4 times as much as 6×10^{23} atoms (1 mole) of hydrogen. In other words, 1 mole of helium must weigh 4 grams. The weight in grams of 1 mole of any element is called the *gram atomic weight* of that element. Thus if we know that the atomic weight of an element is (say) 23, we know that 1 gram atomic weight, or 23 grams, will be the weight of 6×10^{23} atoms (1 mole) of that element.

Similarly, if we know that the molecular weight of a compound is (say) 18, we know that 1 gram molecular weight, or 18 grams, will be the weight of 6×10^{23} molecules (1 mole) of those molecules. A mole of water contains 6×10^{23} molecules of water. Each molecule of water (H_2O) contains 2 atoms of hydrogen and 1 atom of oxygen. Therefore a mole of water contains 12×10^{23} atoms of hydrogen and 6×10^{23} atoms of oxygen. If 6×10^{23} atoms of hydrogen weigh 1 gram, then 12×10^{23} atoms weigh 2 grams. One mole of oxygen weighs 16 grams (1 gram atomic weight). So 1 mole of water must weigh $2 + 16$, or 18, grams.

PROBLEMS

1. Use the Periodic Table on page 78 to find the number of grams in one mole of each of the following compounds.[2]

   a. HCl c. H_2SO_4 e. $CuSO_4$

   b. NH_3 d. $K_2Cr_2O_7$

2. If a pencil weighs 20 grams, how much would a mole of pencils weigh?

REFERENCES

Asimov, Isaac. *A Short History of Chemistry.* ("Science Study Series") Garden City, N.Y.: Doubleday & Co., Inc. (Anchor Books), 1965.

Flaschen, Steward S. *Search and Research: The Story of the Chemical Elements.* Boston: Allyn & Bacon, Inc., 1965.

Jaffe, Bernard. *Crucibles: The Story of Chemicals from Ancient Alchemy to Nuclear Fission.* New York: Simon & Schuster, 1948.

McCormick, Jack. *Atoms, Energy, and Machines.* ("Creative Education Series") New York: American Museum of Natural History, 1962.

Pauling, Linus. *The Architecture of Molecules.* San Francisco: W. H. Freeman and Co., 1964.

Pimentel, G. C. (ed.). *Chemistry: An Experimental Science.* San Francisco: W. H. Freeman and Co., 1963.

Romer, Alfred. *The Restless Atom.* ("Science Study Series") Garden City, N.Y.: Doubleday & Co., Inc. (Anchor Books), 1960.

---

[2]Elements and atomic weights not listed in your Periodic Table are chromium (Cr), 52.0 and copper (Cu), 63.5.

Investigating Properties of Chemical Families

You have seen that the Periodic Table is arranged in families of elements, and that elements are placed within families on the basis of their atomic number and their electron grouping. All elements of a family, however, do not "behave" in exactly the same way. Nor do all elements of a family have exactly the same chemical and physical properties. Aluminum, a member of the boron family, is used to make cooking utensils. Yet thallium, a member of the same family, is used as an insecticide. Nitrogen is part of the air we breathe. But arsenic is a well-known poison. Carbon forms compounds in living things, while most lead compounds are poisonous.

It would therefore be dangerous and very difficult to test for the properties of all elements in our modified table. But we can find several elements that may be safely used to illustrate the similarity of chemical reactions within families of elements. It is important not only to observe the reactions, but also to bring our model of atoms into agreement with the observations. Chemical reactions involve a rearrangement of electrons, and we must consider the effect of this rearrangement on atoms.

Ionization Reactions

You have learned that the number of electrons in an atom is equal to the number of protons as long as the atom remains electrically neutral. If atoms gain electrons they become negatively charged. And if they lose electrons they become positively charged. The process in which atoms become electrically charged is called *ionization*. When an atom becomes electrically charged it is called an *ion*.

Compare the structures of neutral atoms with their ions, as illustrated in Figures 5 · 1 and 5 · 2.

Figure 5 · 1. The sodium atom is electrically neutral because it has an equal number of electrons and protons. The sodium ion, however, has a positive charge because it has 11 protons and only 10 electrons.

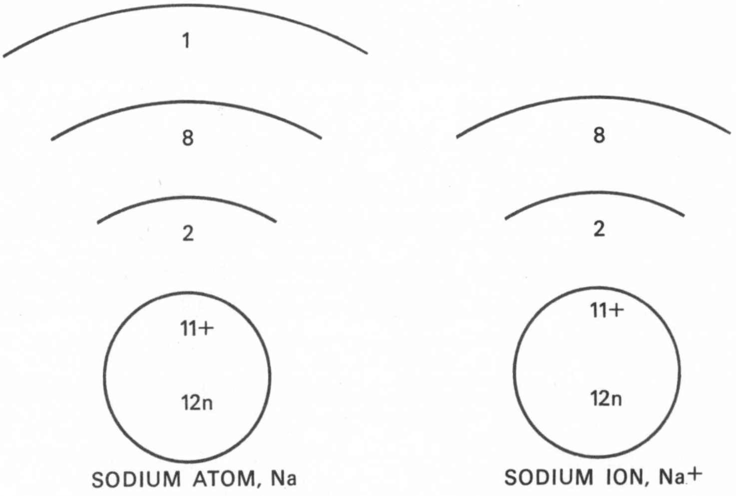

SODIUM ATOM, Na   SODIUM ION, Na+

Figure 5 · 2. The fluorine atom is electrically neutral because it has an equal number of electrons and protons. The fluorine ion has a negative charge because it has 10 electrons and only 9 protons.

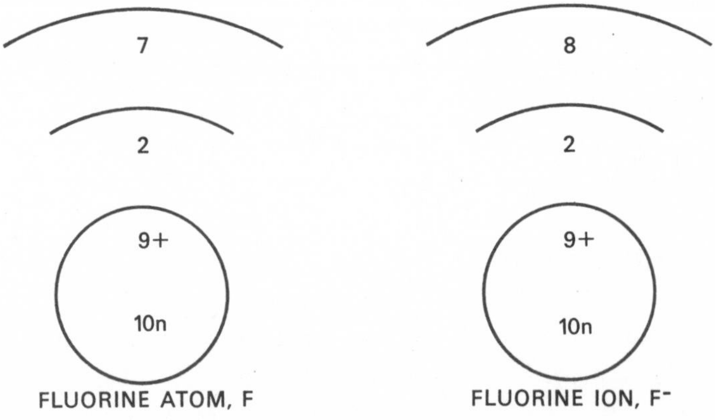

FLUORINE ATOM, F   FLUORINE ION, F−

The sodium and fluorine ions shown have achieved an electron grouping like that of neon—sodium by losing an electron, and fluorine by gaining an electron. All members of a family tend to form ions having the same charge as shown in Figure 5·3.

Lithium Family	Beryllium Family	Fluorine Family
Lithium loses one electron to form Li^{+1}	Beryllium loses two electrons to form Be^{+2}	Fluorine gains one electron to form F^{-1}
Sodium loses one electron to form Na^{+1}	Magnesium loses two electrons to form Mg^{+2}	Chlorine gains one electron to form Cl^{-1}
Potassium loses one electron to form K^{+1}	Calcium loses two electrons to form Ca^{+2}	Bromine gains one electron to form Br^{-1}
Rubidium loses one electron to form Rb^{+1}	Strontium loses two electrons to form Sr^{+2}	Iodine gains one electron to form I^{-1}
Cesium loses one electron to form Cs^{+1}	Barium loses two electrons to form Ba^{+2}	
	Radium loses two electrons to form Ra^{+2}	

Figure 5·3. Ions formed by three families.

INVESTIGATION 7: Conductivity of Solutions

MATERIALS (per team)
  8 jars or beakers, 250-ml
  Conductivity indicator, battery-operated
  Solutions:
   Sodium chloride (NaCl)
   Hydrochloric acid (HCl)
   Sodium hydroxide (NaOH)
   Methyl alcohol (CH_3OH)
   Table sugar ($C_{12}H_{22}O_{11}$)
   Potassium bromide (KBr)
   Barium chloride ($BaCl_2$)

Figure 5 · 4. Predict what will happen to the light on the conductivity indicator when the electrodes are placed in each solution.

Herb Comess

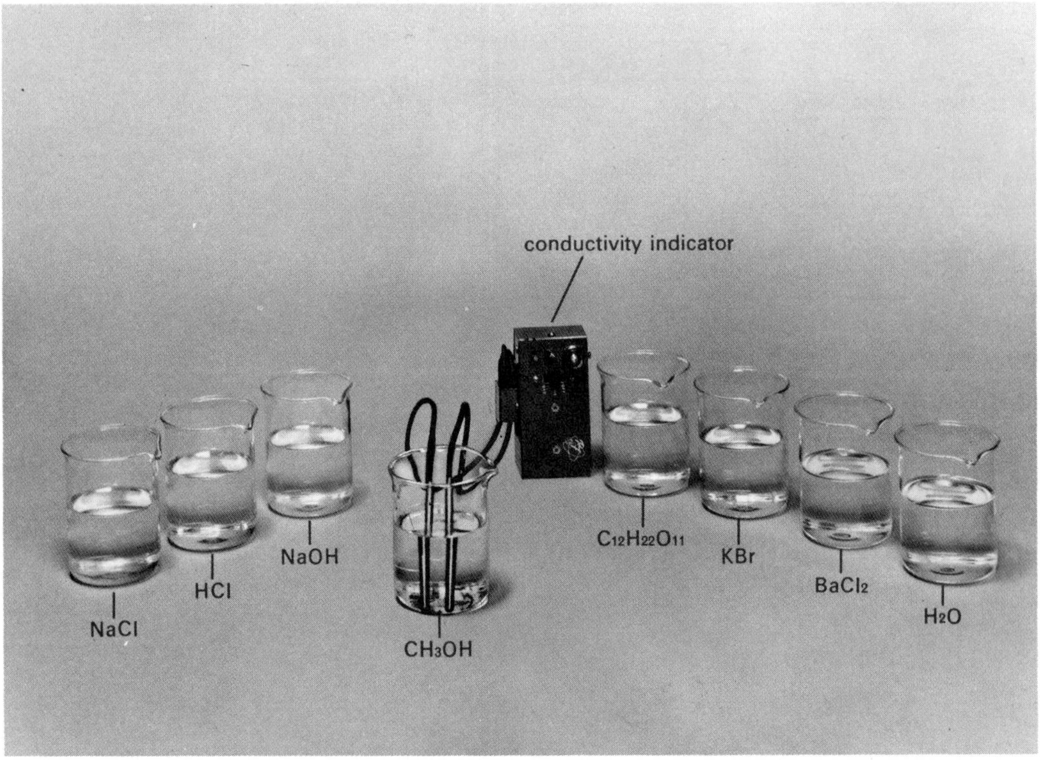

PROCEDURES

A. Arrange a series of eight jars or beakers (Figure 5 · 4), each containing one of the solutions listed. Label each jar. Pour some distilled water into the eighth beaker. Copy the chart shown in Figure 5 · 5.

B. Place the two electrodes of the conductivity indicator in one of the solutions (Figure 5 · 4). Record your observations on the chart. Wipe the electrodes carefully, and test another solution. Record your observations. Repeat with each solution.

Figure 5 · 5.

SOLUTION		GLOW OF LIGHT BULB		
		Bright	*Dim*	*None*
Sodium chloride	NaCl			
Hydrochloric acid	HCl			
Sodium hydroxide	NaOH			
Methyl alcohol	CH_3OH			
Table sugar	$C_{12}H_{22}O_{11}$			
Potassium bromide	KBr			
Barium chloride	$BaCl_2$			
Water	H_2O			

INTERPRETATIONS

1. Which elements listed seem to form compounds that conduct electricity?
2. Recall that elements in the lithium family lose electrons, and elements in the fluorine family gain electrons more easily than do elements in other families. Is the ease with which an element gains or loses electrons related to the conducting ability of a solution containing a compound of that element? If so, describe the relationship.

3. Name some other compounds that should conduct electricity. If you test your hypotheses, be sure to check with your teacher first.

4. Compare the conductivity of the dry chemicals with the conductivity of the same chemicals in solution. Explain any differences noted.

5. Describe a model that might explain why certain solutions are able to conduct electricity while others are not.

Acids and Bases

The structure of water is a key to understanding the behavior of materials we call acids, bases, and salts. Most water particles are molecules. Only a small minority are ions. Consider the following equation:

$$HOH \rightleftharpoons H^+ + OH^-$$

The heavy arrow pointing to the left indicates that most water particles exist as molecules (HOH or H_2O) while only a few hydrogen ions (H^+) and hydroxide ions (OH^-) are present. Thus water is said to be weakly ionized. Note that the oxygen atom and one of the hydrogen atoms have such a strong attraction for each other that the two are written together—they form one ion. There are so few ions in pure water that only very sensitive equipment can detect them. The attraction between H^+ and OH^- ions is strong. These two ions combine more easily than they separate.

What happens when we put some sodium hydroxide ($NaOH$) into a beaker of water? Sodium hydroxide is made up of ions—even in the solid state. When placed in water, these ions become free to move about. We can write this as an equation, as we did for the ionization of water, above. But since *all* of the sodium hydroxide separates into ions, we use only one arrow, pointing to the right.

$$NaOH \longrightarrow Na^+ + OH^-$$

When both water and sodium hydroxide are in the same solution, we can write:

$$HOH \rightleftharpoons H^+ + OH^-$$
$$NaOH \longrightarrow Na^+ + OH^-$$

The hydrogen ion from the water is likely to combine with a hydroxide ion either from the water or from the sodium hydroxide. As a result, a water molecule is formed. Adding the sodium hydroxide to the water greatly increases the concentration of hydroxide ions. A substance that produces an excess of hydroxide ions (OH^-) in water is called a *base*.

If we add hydrochloric acid to the water instead of sodium hydroxide, the effect is quite different. Hydrochloric acid ionizes almost completely; we indicate this by a heavy arrow to the right.

$$HCl \rightleftharpoons H^+ + Cl^-$$

When the ionization reactions for both HCl and H_2O are considered at the same time, we write:

$$HOH \rightleftharpoons H^+ + OH^-$$

$$HCl \rightleftharpoons H^+ + Cl^-$$

The hydroxide ion from water is likely to combine with a hydrogen ion either from the water or from the hydrochloric acid. And again a water molecule is formed. Adding hydrochloric acid to water decreases the already small concentration of hydroxide ions and produces a large concentration of hydrogen ions. A substance that produces an excess of hydrogen ions (H^+) in water is called an *acid*.

The greater the concentration of free H^+ ions produced, the stronger the acid. Strong acids and bases are highly *corrosive*. They can cause painful burns and damage to clothing.

Since the properties of an acid depend upon the presence of H^+ ions, we can expect to find hydrogen in all acids. On the other hand, hydrogen also is part of the OH^- ion, which we find in bases. The difference between molecules of acids and those of bases depends upon the way hydrogen is attached to the rest of the molecule. In acids, a hydrogen separates from the rest of the molecule. In bases, the hydrogen is so strongly attached to an oxygen atom that the two stay together when the molecule breaks apart to form ions.

Note that hydrogen is a family by itself in the Periodic Table. Its behavior is a little different from that of any other element. Hydrogen is the lightest known gas. If enough pressure is applied to a quantity of hydrogen gas, it becomes a liquid and can be used as rocket fuel. Yet when equal amounts of H^+ and OH^- ions are present, the product is water.

INVESTIGATION 8: Testing for Acids and Bases

MATERIALS (per student)
   4 small jars or beakers
   Dilute solution of NaOH
   Dilute solution of HCl
   Salt water
   Litmus paper (red and blue)

PROCEDURES

A. Label four beakers or jars as follows: *NaOH, HCl, Salt water, Tap water.* Pour approximately 10 ml of each liquid into the proper beaker.

B. Copy the chart shown in Figure 5·6 in your notebook. Dip both red and blue litmus paper into each liquid, and record your observations on the chart.

	NaOH	HCl	Salt water	Tap water
Red litmus				
Blue litmus				

Figure 5 · 6.

The results of this test should be kept in your notebook for future reference.

The Formation of Salt: Neutralization

When an acid and a base are placed together in solution, a reaction occurs in which water and a salt are formed. If the acid is HCl and the base is NaOH, we can represent what happens with the following equations:

$$HCl \longrightarrow H^+ + Cl^-$$
$$NaOH \longrightarrow Na^+ + OH^-$$

Or the reaction can be shown with a simpler equation:

$$HCl \quad + \quad NaOH \longrightarrow HOH \quad + \quad NaCl$$

(hydrochloric acid)	(sodium hydroxide)	(water)	(sodium chloride)

Whenever an acid and a base combine to form water and a salt, the reaction is called a *neutralization reaction.* If the proper amount of acid is added to any base, almost all of the H^+ ions in the acid will combine with almost all of the OH^- ions in the base. The concentration of the remaining unattached H^+ and OH^- ions will be the same as in pure water. A solution that shows no surplus of H^+ or OH^- ions is called neutral. That is why the reaction of a base with an acid is called neutralization.

Notice that acids furnish not only H^+ ions but also some negatively charged ions to the solution. In the example above, HCl provides Cl^- ions. On the other hand, bases furnish not only OH^- ions but also some positively charged ions. In the example above, NaOH provides Na^+ ions. As long as water is present, these Na^+ and Cl^- ions remain free. But if the water evaporates, the ions will be attracted to each other (they have opposite charges) and form crystals of salt.

There are many kinds of acids and bases. Thus there are many different kinds of salts. In everyday conversation, when we talk about salt we are usually referring to sodium chloride—table salt. Yet sodium cyanide, a deadly poison, is also a salt. It is formed from sodium hydroxide and hydrocyanic acid. A few salts and their chemical formulas are

sodium chloride:	NaCl	potassium iodide:	KI
sodium cyanide:	NaCN	lithium fluoride:	LiF

Sodium and chlorine are poisonous substances. Yet table salt is an essential part of the diet of man and of many other animals. Obviously sodium chloride must be different in some way from a simple mixture of sodium and chlorine. Salts are compounds. And in sodium chloride, sodium and chloride *ions* combine because of their opposite electric charges. If the elements sodium and chlorine were mixed, you would have *atoms*, not ions.

Neutralization and many other chemical reactions might be viewed as the mischievous actions of demons. Or they might be explained with a different model. A satisfactory model must account for changes in properties resulting from chemical reactions.

INVESTIGATION 9: Precipitation Reactions

When solutions of certain chemicals are mixed together, they react to form solids called *precipitates*. Precipitates may sink to the bottom of a mixture, or they may remain *in suspension,* giving the mixture a cloudy appearance. Precipitation reactions are useful in chemical analysis.

MATERIALS (per team)
> **8 test tubes**
> **Stock solutions:**
>> **Sulfuric acid (H_2SO_4)**
>> **Sodium hydroxide (NaOH)**
>> **Sodium chloride (NaCl)**
>> **Barium chloride ($BaCl_2$)**
>> **Magnesium chloride ($MgCl_2$)**
>> **Potassium chloride (KCl)**

PROCEDURES

A. In your notebook prepare a chart similar to Figure 5·7. Label the test tubes as follows: $NaCl/H_2SO_4$; $NaCl/NaOH$; $BaCl_2/NaOH$; $BaCl_2/H_2SO_4$; KCl/H_2SO_4; $KCl/NaOH$; $MgCl_2/H_2SO_4$; $MgCl_2/NaOH$. Into each tube pour small amounts (about 5 ml each) of the two solutions indicated on the label.

B. Observe the contents of each tube. On your chart indicate which combinations result in a precipitation reaction (formation of solid material). Also indicate which combinations remain clear.

Figure 5·7.

	NaCl	$BaCl_2$	KCl	$MgCl_2$
H_2SO_4				
NaOH				

INTERPRETATIONS

1. Equations for the combinations are listed below. In some of the combinations, precipitates were formed. In other combinations no evidence of a precipitate was observed. Which of the substances to the right of the arrows do you think formed precipitates?

a. $2NaCl + H_2SO_4 \longrightarrow Na_2SO_4 + 2HCl$

b. $NaCl + NaOH \longrightarrow NaCl + NaOH$

c. $BaCl_2 + H_2SO_4 \longrightarrow 2HCl + BaSO_4$

d. $BaCl_2 + 2NaOH \longrightarrow Ba(OH)_2 + 2NaCl$

e. $2KCl + H_2SO_4 \longrightarrow K_2SO_4 + 2HCl$

f. $KCl + NaOH \longrightarrow NaCl + KOH$

g. $MgCl_2 + H_2SO_4 \longrightarrow 2HCl + MgSO_4$

h. $MgCl_2 + 2NaOH \longrightarrow Mg(OH)_2 + 2NaCl$

2. From your observations, which of the following combinations do you think would result in a precipitation reaction? Which would not?

a. elements in the lithium family and sulfuric acid

b. elements in the beryllium family and sulfuric acid

c. elements in the lithium family and sodium hydroxide

d. elements in the beryllium family and sodium hydroxide

Balancing Equations

Chemical equations are said to be balanced when the number of atoms of each element to the left of the arrow equals the number of atoms of that element to the right of the arrow. Remember that *one* sodium ion will combine with *one* chlorine ion. So, if hydrochloric acid reacts with sodium hydroxide, we can write:

$$HCl + NaOH \longrightarrow NaCl + HOH$$

But it takes *two* chlorine ions to combine with *one* ion of magnesium (Mg). So, if hydrochloric acid reacts with magnesium hydroxide, we must write:

$$2HCl + Mg(OH)_2 \longrightarrow MgCl_2 + 2HOH$$

Chemical reactions occur in this way because different elements may form ions with different charges. Molecules are electrically neutral and must have equal amounts of positive and negative charge.

As a general rule, elements that tend to lose electrons combine with elements that tend to gain electrons. Thus both kinds of elements tend to achieve an electron grouping like that of an inert gas. Elements in the hydrogen, lithium, beryllium, and boron families tend to form compounds with elements in the nitrogen, oxygen, and fluorine families. Since carbon may either lose or gain as many as four electrons, it forms compounds with most of the elements. The chemistry of carbon compounds is complicated and will be considered at a later time.

In pure form, the elements hydrogen, nitrogen, oxygen, and all of the members of the fluorine family form molecules that contain two atoms. These are diatomic (two atom) molecules, and they are written as follows: H_2, N_2, O_2, F_2, Cl_2, Br_2, I_2. You need to use this information so that you can balance chemical equations in which these elements are present.

Balancing equations is not necessarily difficult, but it does require that certain rules be followed. Consider the reaction between calcium (Ca) and oxygen (O_2):

$$Ca + O_2 \longrightarrow \; ?$$

Calcium is in the beryllium family and will react in a 1-to-1 ratio with elements in the oxygen family. An *incorrect* equation is:

$$Ca + O_2 \longrightarrow CaO_2$$

Calcium combines with oxygen in the ratio of 1 to 1, not 1 to 2. In other words, as far as we know, the compound CaO_2 does not exist. The correct equation for the combination of calcium and oxygen is as follows:

$$2Ca + O_2 \longrightarrow 2CaO$$

Before you can write a complete equation for a reaction, you must know the correct formulas for the compounds involved in the reaction.

Numbers slightly below and to the right of the symbol for an element or a *radical* (two or more elements that act as one) refer *only* to that particular element or radical. Examples: In a molecule of Na_2SO_4 there are two atoms of sodium, one atom of sulfur, and four atoms of oxygen. In $Ba(OH)_2$, the number 2 refers to everything inside the parentheses, the (OH) radical. Therefore, the molecule contains one atom of barium. two atoms of hydrogen, and two atoms of oxygen.

A number to the left of, and level with, the symbols for a compound multiplies *all* atoms in the compound by that number. For example, 2HCl represents two molecules of HCl or a total of two atoms of hydrogen (H) and two atoms of chlorine (Cl).

PROBLEMS

1. Examine each of the combinations listed in Interpretation 1, page 93. Determine whether or not equal numbers of each kind of atom appear on both sides of the arrow.

2. Predict the number of atoms of each element in the lithium family which would be needed to combine with one atom of oxygen.

3. Write balanced chemical equations for each of the following:
   a. Mg + Cl_2 $\longrightarrow$
   b. $2Li$ + Br_2 $\longrightarrow$
   c. $2Ba$ + O_2 $\longrightarrow$
   d. Ca + S $\longrightarrow$
   e. Ca + I_2 $\longrightarrow$
   f. NaI + $AgNO_3$ $\longrightarrow$
   g. Na_2S + $BaCl_2$ $\longrightarrow$

REFERENCES

Asimov, Isaac. *The Search for the Elements.* New York: Basic Books, 1962.

———. *A Short History of Chemistry.* ("Science Study Series") Garden City, N.Y.: Doubleday & Co., Inc. (Anchor Books), 1965.

Davis, Kenneth S., and Day, John Arthur. *Water: The Mirror of Science.* ("Science Study Series") Garden City, N.Y.: Doubleday & Co., Inc. (Anchor Books), 1961.

Flaschen, Steward S. *Search and Research: The Story of the Chemical Elements.* Boston: Allyn & Bacon, Inc., 1965.

Helfman, Mrs. Elizabeth S. *Water for the World.* New York: David McKay Co., Inc. (Longmans, Green & Co., Inc.), 1960.

McClellan, A. L. (ed.). *Chemistry: An Experimental Science.* San Francisco: W. H. Freeman and Co., 1963.

Pauling, Linus. *The Architecture of Molecules.* San Francisco: W. H. Freeman and Co., 1964.

Investigating a Compound

INVESTIGATION 10: Concept of Analysis

Since compounds are combinations of elements, *analysis* requires the taking apart, or the breaking down, of compounds so that the elements can be identified. Chemists are frequently faced with the problem of analyzing unknown compounds. Various methods may be used in analysis. These methods range from simple heating to highly technical processes that require special equipment.

In this investigation each team will be given a sample of an "unknown compound" to analyze. For convenience, we will call the compound "bluestone."

CAUTION: *The "bluestone" is poisonous if taken internally.*

MATERIALS (per team)
Baby-food jar with lid
Crushed bluestone (small baby-food jar, about half-full)
A few pieces of bluestone
Graduated cylinder
Watch glass
2 small test tubes
Iron filings, 5 ml
Iron nail
Steel wool
Solution of barium chloride

PROCEDURES

A. Pour 25 ml of water into a baby-food jar and add 20 g of crushed bluestone. Screw the cap onto the jar tightly. Shake the jar several times and note the color of the solution. Record your observations. Set the jar aside until the next time the class meets.

B. Examine several pieces of bluestone. Can you detect any similarity among them? Describe in your notebook the appearance of the bluestone, including color, shape, and other characteristics you think might be important. Make a sketch of a piece of bluestone in your notebook.

C. At the beginning of the next class period, observe the solution in the jar again. Did the bluestone dissolve?

D. Using a graduated cylinder, measure out 5 ml of the bluestone solution and carefully pour it into a watch glass. Save the remainder of the solution. Allow the watch glass to sit until the next time the class meets, so that the solution loses water by evaporation.

INTERPRETATIONS

1. Explain the reappearance of the bluestone in Procedure D.
2. Examine pieces of bluestone recovered in the watch glass. Compare them with the pieces examined in Procedure B. Are there any differences? If so, explain them.

PROCEDURES (continued)

E. Pour bluestone solution into a small test tube until the tube is about half-full. Slowly add iron filings to the solution. Shake the test tube, and record any changes. Continue adding filings and shaking the tube until no further change occurs.

F. Pour 5 ml of bluestone solution into a second test tube. Polish a nail with steel wool, and place it in the tube. After five minutes, remove the nail and inspect it. Compare it with the color of a penny. Record your observations.

INTERPRETATIONS (continued)

3. What is the color of the solution in Procedure E, after iron filings are added?

4. State a hypothesis that will explain this color change.

5. Pour off only the liquid from the first test tube, and examine the filings. Compare the nail with the material on the iron filings.

6. State a hypothesis about the material responsible for the color of bluestone.

PROCEDURES (continued)

G. Empty and rinse one of the test tubes with tap water. Pour bluestone solution from the baby-food jar into the tube until it is half-full. Slowly add a solution of $BaCl_2$ (barium chloride) to the tube until signs of chemical reaction stop. Record your observations.

INTERPRETATIONS (continued)

7. Did the addition of $BaCl_2$ change the color of the bluestone solution? What substance might be present in the bluestone that could form a precipitate with barium?

8. Does the addition of $BaCl_2$ change your hypothesis (Interpretation 6) about the material responsible for the color of bluestone?

9. You have partially analyzed a chemical compound. From the results of your experiments, and from your observations, prepare a written description of bluestone, including the elements that you think make up the compound. Your statement will be judged on the basis of how carefully you have organized experimental results and observations.

INVESTIGATION 11: Gaining Additional Evidence

Your analysis at the end of Investigation 10 has given you some information about the compound we call bluestone. Scientists are usually not satisfied with the results of an experiment until they have carried out many different experiments that give the same results. Only then can they feel confident about their conclusions.

By testing a solution of bluestone for the presence and behavior of ions, you will learn more about the structure of bluestone.

MATERIALS (per team)
> Conductivity indicator
> 50 ml of bluestone solution
> 150-ml beaker or baby-food jar
> 2 electrodes (paper clips and wires)
> 250-ml beaker or baby-food jar
> 150 ml of distilled water
> Dialysis tubing, 20 cm
> 6-volt battery
> 10 ml of barium chloride ($BaCl_2$) solution
> 3 medicine droppers
> Glass microscope slide or glass plate of similar size

PROCEDURES

A. Pour the bluestone solution into the 150-ml beaker. Insert the probes of the conductivity indicator into the solution, and determine whether or not the solution conducts electricity. Record your observation.

INTERPRETATIONS

1. Did the solution conduct electricity? Are ions present in the solution?
2. From the results of the test, can you determine whether or not the color of the solution is caused by the presence of ions?

PROCEDURES (continued)

B. Using the 250-ml beaker, set up apparatus for the separation of ions as shown in Figure 3 · 11, page 60. Pour distilled water into the two halves of the dialysis tubing and into the 250-ml beaker. Pour 10 ml of bluestone solution into the distilled water in the beaker.

C. Before carrying out Procedure D, predict what the result would be if:

   a. the color is caused by negative ions.

   b. the color is caused by positive ions.

   c. the color is not caused by ions at all.

D. Insert an electrode into each half of the dialysis tubing, and connect the electrode wires to the battery. Allow the test to continue for about twenty minutes before disconnecting the electrodes.

E. Write the letters *A* and *B* at the ends of a glass microscope slide (Figure 6 · 1). Place a drop of barium chloride solution near each letter on the slide. Using a clean medicine dropper, obtain a sample of water from the dialysis tubing that was connected

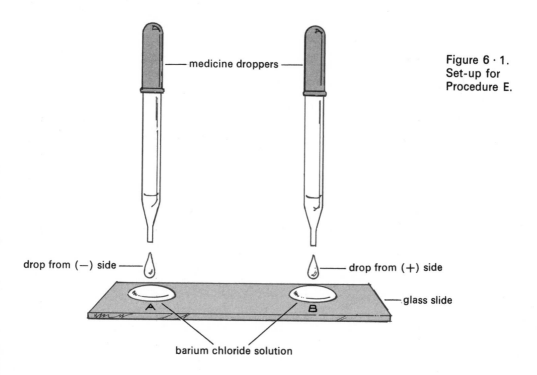

medicine droppers

drop from (−) side

drop from (+) side

glass slide

A

B

barium chloride solution

Figure 6 · 1.
Set-up for
Procedure E.

to the negative side of the battery. Add a drop of this water to the *A* drop of barium chloride solution on the slide. Using a clean dropper, obtain a sample of water from the dialysis tubing that was connected to the positive side of the battery. Add a drop of this water to the *B* drop of barium chloride solution. Record your observations.

INTERPRETATIONS (continued)
3. What can you conclude about the particles that give the solution a blue color?
4. What can you conclude about the particles that react with the barium chloride solution?

INVESTIGATION 12: Problem of Color

You have partially analyzed a compound. In the process you have experienced some of the successes and failures that are typical in scientific research. You have tried to establish a reasonable hypothesis to account for the color of bluestone. Other properties of bluestone, studied in this investigation, should add to your understanding of chemical interaction.

MATERIALS (per team)
    Crushed bluestone
    Evaporating dish
    Ring stand and ring
    Wire gauze
    Bunsen burner or alcohol burner
    Matches
    Small Pyrex test tube
    Test tube holder

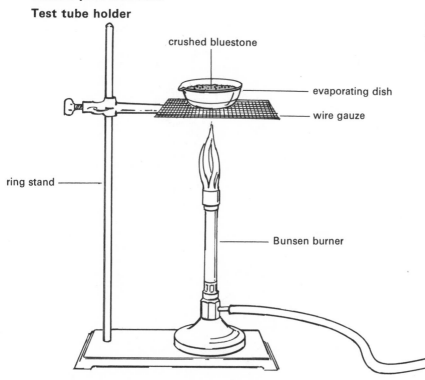

Figure 6 · 2. Set-up for Procedure A.

crushed bluestone

evaporating dish

wire gauze

ring stand

Bunsen burner

PROCEDURES

A. Place a small amount of crushed bluestone in a clean evaporating dish. Set up the apparatus shown in Figure 6 · 2. Heat the dish of bluestone over the burner until the material shows a definite change. Allow it to cool. Record your observations.

B. Place a small amount of powdered bluestone in the bottom of a clean Pyrex test tube. Place the tube in the holder, and heat gently until no further changes occur. Record your observations.

INTERPRETATIONS

1. Compare and explain results observed in Procedures A and B.
2. From these observations, evaluate your hypothesis about the material responsible for the color of bluestone. Under what conditions does bluestone show a blue color?
3. Is the white substance still bluestone?
4. What substances do you believe are in bluestone? What questions about the structure of bluestone still seem unanswered?

INVESTIGATION 13: Role of Energy

Investigations 10 through 12 should have revealed a relationship between the structure of bluestone and its color. Investigation 13 points to still another kind of chemical interaction, the role of energy in chemical reactions.

MATERIALS (per team)
Crushed bluestone
Small Pyrex test tube
Bunsen burner or alcohol burner
Test tube holder
Test tube rack (or a small beaker or baby-food jar to support the tube while it cools)
Medicine dropper

PROCEDURES
A. Place a small amount of bluestone in a clean Pyrex test tube. Place the tube in the holder, and heat until the bluestone turns white. Allow the tube to cool.
B. Hold the tube containing the white form of bluestone exactly as shown in Figure 6·3. Slowly add water, drop by drop,

Herb Comess

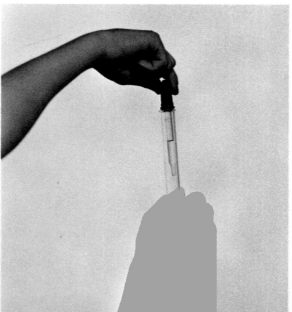

Figure 6 · 3.
Carrying out
Procedure B.

until a definite color change occurs. Note anything that happens as you add water.

INTERPRETATION

1. In addition to a change in color, another kind of change occurred as water was added. Describe this change fully. Try to state a hypothesis that will explain this additional change.

INVESTIGATION 14: Weight Relationships (Optional)

Data gathered in Investigations 12 and 13 suggest that water is involved in the structure of bluestone. If a small amount of water evaporates when a sample of bluestone is heated, part of the sample is blue and part is white. If enough water is added to bluestone, the bluestone will dissolve. Your problem is to determine the ratio of water molecules to molecules of the white material in a pure sample of bluestone crystals. Experiments have shown that the molecular weight of the white material, obtained by heating bluestone, is 160 grams per mole.

Design an experiment that will give you the data needed to calculate the number of water molecules that combine with one molecule of the white material to form pure bluestone crystals. Describe the experiment in your notebook. *Check with your teacher before attempting the experiment*. To make your calculations significant, you must perform weighings with as much precision as possible.

INVESTIGATION 15: Comparing Different Salts (Optional)

So far your research in Section Six has resulted in a partial analysis of bluestone. You have determined some of the elements that form this compound. From your earlier study of acids, bases, and salts, you might suspect that bluestone is a salt, even though it is quite different from ordinary table salt (it is poisonous to man). In Investigation 15 you will compare four salts: sodium chloride ($NaCl$), copper sulfate ($CuSO_4$), potassium sulfate (K_2SO_4), and sodium carbonate (Na_2CO_3).

MATERIALS (per student)
   4 small test tubes
   Sodium chloride (NaCl)
   Copper sulfate (CuSO₄)
   Potassium sulfate (K₂SO₄)
   Sodium carbonate (Na₂CO₃)
   Chemical indicators for acids and bases

PROCEDURES
A. Label the four tubes as follows: *sodium chloride, copper sulfate, potassium sulfate, sodium carbonate*. Pour tap water into the tubes until each is about half-full.
B. Dissolve 1g of each substance in the proper test tube.
C. Test each solution with chemical indicators.

INTERPRETATIONS
1. Describe the results of the indicator test for each solution.
2. Suggest an explanation for any differences noted.

REFERENCES
Holden, Alan, and Singer, Phylis. *Crystals and Crystal Growing.* ("Science Study Series") Garden City, N.Y.: Doubleday & Co., Inc. (Anchor Books), 1960.

Jaffe, Bernard. *Crucibles: The Story of Chemicals from Ancient Alchemy to Nuclear Fission.* New York: Simon & Schuster, 1948.

McClellan, A. L. (ed.). *Chemistry: An Experimental Science.* San Francisco: W. H. Freeman and Co., 1963.

Metcalfe, H. C., and others. *Modern Chemistry.* New York: Holt, Rinehart & Winston, Inc., 1966.

Young, Jay A. *Elements of General Chemistry.* Englewood Cliffs, N.J.: Prentice-Hall, 1960.

The Meaning of Measurement

Science is often described as man's attempt to understand and explain what he observes through his senses. One of the first steps in any scientific activity is observation. Observation often leads us to ask why, how, or what. Without the formulation of questions, we have no science.

Sometimes we may answer questions by making additional observations: What color is it? What does it feel like? Does it make a noise? Does it have an odor or a taste? Such questions can be answered by using one or more of our senses.

But consider another type of question: How big is it? How heavy is it? How hot is it? How fast is it moving? Through the senses you may be able to make rough guesses about such things as size, weight, temperature, and speed. But unless you *compare* your observations with something that is familiar to others, you cannot describe size, weight, and so forth, in a way that has meaning. Accurate observations and the communication of them to others require some standards of measuring.

Do you suppose Cro-Magnon man measured things? What did he need to measure? What might he have used as standards of measure? All that was available to him were the natural objects of his environment—himself, the sun, trees, stones, and so forth.

What did he do when new clothing was needed? Do you suppose an animal was killed and skinned, and its skin was held up to a member of the tribe? In this case the human body was the standard of measure.

When a hunter proved the value of a particular type of spear, other hunters might have wanted one like it. The spear could have been used as a standard for making other spears. When these spears became widely used, perhaps the chief of the tribe announced that "the spear" was to be the measurement standard.

A large, heavy spear could not be used to advantage in hunting small animals; perhaps the weapon needed for this was a stone. How could Cro-Magnon man decide on the size of stone? By hefting it in his hand? By the feel and shape of it? Through trial and error he probably arrived at the right kind of stone for killing an animal of a certain size and a certain distance away.

Figure 7 · 1.
Cro-Magnon men
selecting stones
to be used for
killing birds.

Number Sense

Some ability to understand differences in numbers appears to be present in many animals. This ability has been called number sense. If one of her kittens is removed, a mother cat will usually show that she is aware of the loss. A farmer reported an interesting example of number sense in a crow that often roosted near his barn. If the farmer went into his barn, the crow would fly away and not return until the farmer came out. If the farmer and his hired man entered the barn, the crow would leave and not return until *both* men came out. If three men went in and then came out one at a time, even with long waits in between, the crow would not return until all three had come out.

Could the crow count? What else might have explained the crow's ability to keep track of the number of men in the barn? Perhaps the crow could smell or sense in some other way that a man was still inside. The farmer decided to test this hypothesis. He went into the barn as usual. But the hired man sneaked around to the back without the crow seeing him and entered through another door. The crow flew away and returned when *one* man left through the front door!

Further testing indicated there was a limit to the crow's number sense. When as many as four persons entered the barn and left together, in a combination of three and one or two and two, the crow would return. But when five or more persons entered, the bird apparently lost count and would return even if all but one person remained in the barn.

Some system of counting was necessary before man could develop a system of measurement. We do not know when he learned to count. But it is reasonable to assume that early man at least had the ability to keep track of things by number sense.

Was early man concerned with distance? We can only guess that he measured distance with steps or paces. Long distances could have been measured by keeping a count of how many "suns" rose and set during a given trip.

When man moved from caves into dwellings he himself built, there was a need for measurement during construction. Words were needed to express quantity, size, and distance. Eventually, by using the most convenient object in his environment, man developed the following units of measurement.

Cubit: the distance from the point of the elbow to the tip of the middle finger.

Span: the distance from the tip of the thumb to the tip of the little finger when the fingers are spread out.

Palm: the breadth of four fingers held together.

Digit: the breadth of the index finger or middle finger.

Figure 7 · 2. Units of measure derived from the human body.

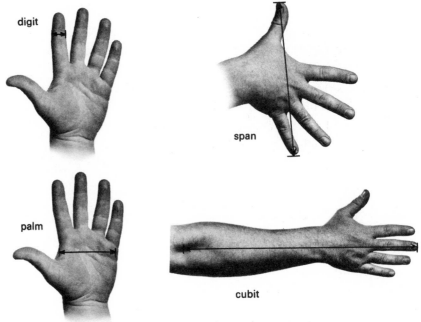

Herb Comess

These measurements—particularly the cubit—were important to the early Babylonians, Hebrews, and Egyptians. If one person was doing all the measuring on a job, the cubit was always the same. But when temples, pyramids, and other large structures requiring the efforts of many men were being built, identical units of measure had to be used. What kind of architecture would have resulted if each worker had measured with his own arms, hands, and fingers?

More precise units of measure were needed, and the measuring rod came into use. The exact length of a rod was usually decided by the local king or pharaoh. One-cubit measuring rods were produced (Figure 7·3).

National Bureau of Standards

Smithsonian Institution

Figure 7·3. *Top:* Five thousand years ago, the Egyptians established the first standard of linear measurement, the cubit. The cubit (meaning "forearm") was equivalent in length to the pharaoh's forearm—about 20.6 inches. The Royal Cubit shown here was made of black granite and divided into spans, palms, digits, and fractions of digits. It was placed in the custody of the royal architect. *Bottom:* Wooden cubit rods were made from the Royal Cubit and were used in building Egypt's great pyramids, tombs, and temples.

The Egyptians also used a simple but clever method to determine the height of the trees needed for ship masts or other tall structures. By setting a stick upright beside a tree, a man could determine the height of the tree on a sunny day. Can you see how he did this?

As the power of Egypt declined, the Roman Empire was expanding. The early Romans were the first to measure distance in *miles. Mile* is short for the Latin words *millė passuum*, meaning thousand paces. The Romans borrowed the term *foot* from the Greeks, and divided the foot into *inches* (the breadth of the thumb). The measurements of the Roman foot and inch are not quite the same as ours.

It is easy to see how the foot was derived, but, like other body measurements, it varied from one man to another. So the Romans used measuring rods. These were kept in the temples. With the fall of the Roman Empire, many of these temples were destroyed and the measuring rods were lost. With the breakdown of central government, the small towns and hamlets had to use their own standards of measurement.

In Western Europe, local lords and barons came into power, and the strongest among them became kings. These monarchs set their own standards of measure. They still used body measurements—often the king's personal measurements. King Henry I of England (1068–1135) defined the *yard* as the distance from the tip of his nose to the end of his thumb when his arm was fully extended to one side. A system of weights was developed with stones and crude balances. The term *stone* is still used in England today as a standard weight. (One stone equals fourteen pounds.)

In the latter part of the eighteenth century leading citizens of the new Republic of France decided there was a need for more precise measures—measures that would not be dependent on the length of someone's forearm, and so forth. The standards would be used throughout France and made available to other nations.

It was decided that the basic unit of linear measure would be one twenty-millionth of the length of the meridian that passes through Paris. (A meridian is an imaginary half-circle on the earth's surface, extending from the North Pole to the South Pole. See Figure 7 · 4.) This distance was the first *meter*. In 1791 surveying operations were begun to determine the length of this unit. Unfortunately an error was made in the calculations, and a new meter had to be established. Finally the correct distance was carefully measured off on a bar of platinum-iridium; two marks to indicate the exact length of the standard meter were engraved on it. This bar was called the International Prototype Meter. It was kept under triple lock and key in the Pavilion de Bretueuil at Sevres, France, the home of the International Bureau of Weights and Measures. Carefully made, certified copies of this meter were given to countries using the new standards in the metric system.

In the twentieth century, as industry and science began to require more accurate measurements, a new official standard was adopted. In 1960 the General Conferences on Weights and Measures met in Paris and adopted an official *standard meter*, which is based on a certain wave length of light.[1] Using complex equipment, it is now possible to make measurements of length accurate

---

[1]The nature of light waves will be considered in Section Twelve.

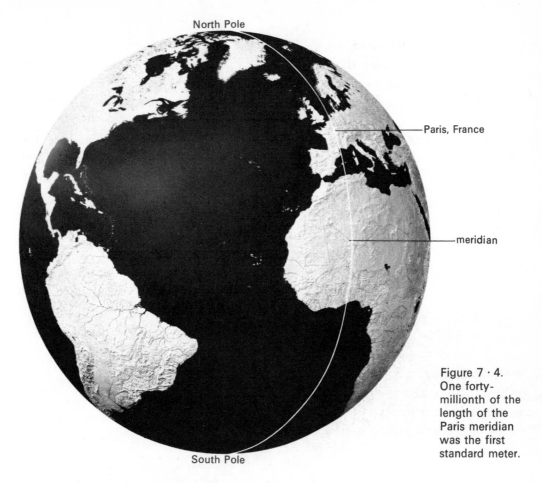

North Pole

Paris, France

meridian

South Pole

Figure 7 · 4.
One forty-
millionth of the
length of the
Paris meridian
was the first
standard meter.

to one part in a hundred million.

Today we have highly accurate standards for weighing and measuring objects. Yet we still use body measurements. We still pace off distances, and women still estimate the yardage in a piece of material by using an approximation of King Henry's yard.

In future investigations you will learn more about the metric system and its use. A table is included in an appendix at the back of the book, for your use in converting measurements from the English to the metric system.

All standards of weights and measures are arbitrary. Somewhere, at some time, someone simply decided that a certain unit of measure would be useful. If it was convenient to use and to duplicate, it stood a good chance of becoming a standard unit.

PROBLEMS

1. Today the metric system of measurement is used in all parts of the world for most scientific work. Why do you think most scientists, regardless of nationality, agree on the use of one system of measurement?

2. Most of the non-English-speaking nations have adopted the metric system. England is changing to the metric system, but the United States still uses the English system. Do you think we should change our standards of measure? Give reasons why we should or should not change.

3. Explain how the Egyptians were able to find the height of a tree by knowing the length of a stick's shadow.

INVESTIGATION 16: Measurement of Length and Area

This investigation will give you an opportunity to experience some of the difficulties in measuring that might have confronted a student living during the eighteenth century. It will also allow you to use some modern methods of measurement.

MATERIALS (per team)
  Yardstick
  Meterstick

PROCEDURES
A. Measure the length and width of a desk or table, using units of body measurement—the cubit, span, and palm. Record your data.
B. Compute the area of the desk or table in square cubits, square spans, and square palms.
C. Measure the same desk or table in inches, feet, and yards, using a yardstick. Using a meterstick, repeat the measurements in millimeters, centimeters, and meters.

INTERPRETATIONS
1. What are the advantages and disadvantages of using your own units of body measurement (cubit, span, and so forth) in reporting measurements?
2. Which system of units did you find most useful? Which is most accurate?
3. What is meant by the statement that "All measurements are estimates"?

INVESTIGATION 17: Determining the Volume of Solids

The space that an object or a substance occupies is called its *volume*. It is relatively easy to determine the volume of liquids by using a graduated cylinder. Determining the volume of a solid requires different techniques. Recall that you found the area of a

Figure 7 · 5.

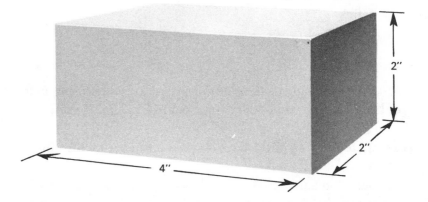

desk top or table top by multiplying the length by width. You determined the area in square cubits, square spans, square feet, square centimeters, and so forth. To determine the volume of a door or other rectangular object, you must multiply the area of the object by its depth. For practice, suppose you wish to find the volume of the rectangular object shown in Figure 7 · 5.

The area of one of the rectangular sides is 4 inches x 2 inches, or 8 square inches. The volume is 8 square inches x 2 inches, or 16 *cubic* inches. Thus the dimensions involved are length, width, area, and volume. "Cubic" should not be a new term for you (sugar cubes, ice cubes). Cubic measurement is necessary in determining the volume of solids.

MATERIALS (per team)
  3 rectangular solids of different sizes
  Ruler calibrated in inches and centimeters
  50- or 100-ml graduated cylinder
  Overflow can (Figure 7 · 6)

Yard of thread
Graph paper
Nails, marble, and other objects small enough to fit in
  graduated cylinder
Straight pin or fine wire
Small pieces of wood (irregular shapes)
Sugar cubes

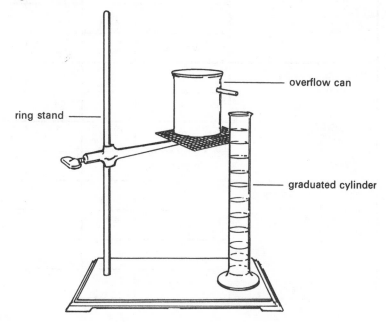

Figure 7 · 6.
Set-up for
Procedures C–F.

PROCEDURES

A. In your notebook, copy the chart shown in Figure 7 · 7.

B. Number the solids. Use your ruler to determine the volume of each solid in cubic inches and in cubic centimeters. Record this data on your chart.

C. Place the graduated cylinder under the spout of the overflow can. Fill the can with tap water until water begins to flow from the spout. When the flow has stopped, empty the graduated cylinder and place it under the spout again.

D. Tie a thread around Solid 1, and lower it carefully into the water. If the solid does not sink, hold it under water with a pin or other small probe.

Figure 7 · 7.

	Trial Number	Solids		
		1	2	3
Volume in cubic inches	1			
	2			
	3			
	average			
Volume in cubic centimeters	1			
	2			
	3			
	average			
Volume of displaced water in milliliters	1			
	2			
	3			
	average			

E. Keep the solid completely submerged until the water has stopped flowing into the cylinder. Then carefully measure the amount of water in the cylinder.

Recall from Section Two that water has a slightly concave surface when confined in a narrow cylinder. This could cause some error in determining volume. The accepted scientific practice is to take the reading at the lowest point of the curve (Figure 7 · 8). It is also important that the cylinder be on a level surface. The reading should be taken at eye level.

Repeat Procedures D through E two more times. Record on your chart the volumes for each of the three trials with Solid 1. Calculate the average volume obtained with each method.

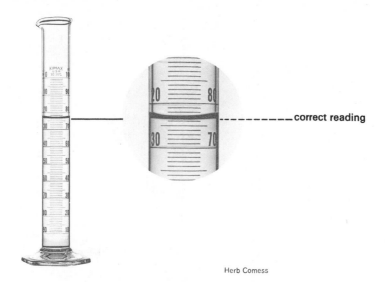

Figure 7 · 8.
The correct read-
ing of a gradu-
ated cylinder is
taken from the
lowest point of
the curve formed
by the liquid.

correct reading

Herb Comess

F. Repeat Procedures B through E for Solid 2 and Solid 3. Be
    sure to record the data for each of the three trials with each
    solid.

G. On graph paper construct the graph shown in Figure 7 · 9A.
    Use the vertical axis of the graph for volumes in cubic inches
    and the horizontal axis for the number of milliliters of water
    displaced (collected in the graduated cylinder). Plot the *aver-
    age* of the three trials for each solid. Beginning at zero, draw
    a line connecting the three average points.

H. Using another piece of graph paper, repeat Procedure G, but
    plot the values for volume in cubic centimeters against volume
    of displaced water in milliliters (Figure 7 · 9B).

INTERPRETATIONS

1. Note the relationship between the volumes in cubic inches,
    cubic centimeters, and milliliters. Which system—English or
    metric—seems to be the easiest to use in finding the volume
    of a solid?

2. Carefully compare the two graphs, and describe any differ-
    ences or similarities.

3. In Procedure G were you able to draw a straight line from
    zero through the three average points? If not, how can you
    explain the results?

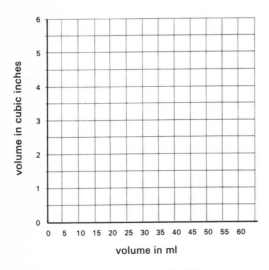

Figure 7 · 9A.

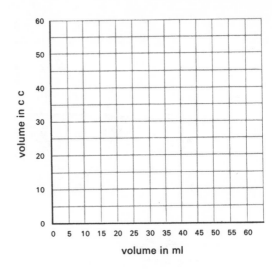

Figure 7 · 9B.

PROCEDURES (continued)

I. You may wish to determine the volumes of other objects. The overflow can is not needed for objects small enough to be placed directly in the graduated cylinder. Pour enough water into the graduated cylinder to completely submerge the object. (Usually this can be done if the cylinder is about half-full.) Read and record the volume of the water. Submerge the object in the water, and again take a reading from the cylinder. If the object floats, hold it under the water with a pin or fine wire. What is the volume of the object?

PROBLEMS

1. Use a ruler (English and metric) and the water-displacement method to measure the volume of each of the following:
    a. an irregular shaped piece of wood
    b. a cube of sugar

2. Which method of measuring volume did you find most useful in Problem 1? Which system—English or metric—did you find most convenient?

INVESTIGATION 18: Mass and Volume of Water

Matter is described as any substance that has mass (weight) and occupies space (volume). For now we will use the words *mass* and *weight* as if they had the same meaning. Later in the course, understanding the difference between mass and weight will become important.

The relationship between mass and volume will be examined in this investigation.

MATERIALS (per team)
> Balance sensitive to 0.1 gram
> 50- or 100-ml graduated cylinder
> Sheet of ordinary graph paper
> Red pencil

PROCEDURES

A. Copy the chart shown in Figure 7 · 10 in your notebook.

Figure 7 · 10.

Trial	Mass of graduated cylinder in grams	Mass of graduated cylinder and water in grams	Mass of water in grams	Volume of water in milliliters
1				
2				
3				
4				
5				
Average				

B. Weigh the graduated cylinder, and record its mass on the chart.
C. Pour some water into the cylinder. Weigh the cylinder with the water in it. Record the combined mass on the chart.
D. Determine the mass of the water by subtracting the mass of the cylinder from the mass of the water and the cylinder.

E. Determine the volume of water in the cylinder. Remember to keep the cylinder level and to take readings at the low point of the meniscus (the curve of the water's surface). Record on the chart.

F. Repeat Procedures C, D, and E four more times, using a different volume of water in each trial. Record the data on the chart.

G. Plot values for the mass and volume of water in each trial on ordinary graph paper. Use the vertical axis for mass and the horizontal axis for volume. This will give you five points on the graph. Beginning at zero, draw a line connecting these points. Calculate the average mass and the average volume of water. Using a red pencil, plot this point on the graph. Beginning at zero, draw a straight red line through the average point; extend this line as far as possible beyond the average point. Keep the graph in your notebook.

INTERPRETATIONS

1. Divide the *average* mass of water obtained in all trials by the *average* volume for all trials: $\dfrac{M}{V} = ?$ Compare the average value for $\dfrac{M}{V}$ obtained by your team with the average values obtained by other teams.

2. What relationship appears to exist between the mass of water in grams and its volume in milliliters?

INVESTIGATION 19: Mass and Volume of Liquids Other Than Water

This investigation is similar to Investigation 18. Keeping this in mind, predict what a graph developed as in Investigation 18 will show when liquids other than water are used.

MATERIALS (per team)
Balance sensitive to 0.1 gram
50- or 100-ml graduated cylinder
50 ml alcohol (ditto fluid)
50 ml white Karo syrup

PROCEDURES

A. Using the procedures described in Investigation 18, determine the mass of three different volumes of ditto fluid. Do the same for three volumes of white Karo syrup. Plot the three volume points for each liquid on the graph you made in Investigation 18. Draw a line connecting the zero point and the three points for ditto fluid. Draw another line connecting the zero point and the points for Karo syrup.

INTERPRETATIONS

1. Examine the red line on the graph, which shows the relation of mass and volume of *water*. Select several points on the horizontal axis, and determine the value of the ratio $\frac{M}{V}$ for each of these volumes. You can read the mass for each volume from the graph. Note that each point on this line represents a number you can obtain by dividing the number of grams of water by the number of milliliters of water. That is,

$$\frac{\text{number of grams of water}}{\text{number of ml of water}} = \text{number of grams per ml.}$$

What is the value of $\frac{M}{V}$ for each of the points you have selected?

2. Determine the value of $\frac{M}{V}$ for at least three different points on

the line drawn for the relationship between mass and volume of ditto fluid. Do the same for Karo syrup.

How does the value of $\frac{M}{V}$ for ditto fluid compare with the value of $\frac{M}{V}$ for water? How does the value of $\frac{M}{V}$ for Karo syrup compare with that for water?

The mass of material found in one unit of volume is called the *density* of the material for that volume. Here, density depends upon two kinds of units—units of mass and units of volume. Thus we can express the density of water as 1 gram per milliliter, 62.5 pounds per cubic foot, or in any other units we may choose. But we must know how many units of mass are contained in a given number of units of volume.

INVESTIGATION 20: Determining the Density of Various Objects (Optional)

In this investigation you will be given little or no instruction. If you have learned the concepts presented in the last few investigations, this should not prove too difficult.

MATERIALS (per student or team)
>   Artgum eraser
>   Several marbles
>   Small rock
>   Cube of cane sugar
>   Large nails held together with rubber bands
>   Small piece of Styrofoam, irregular shape
>   Ice cube
>   Graph paper

PROCEDURES

A. Determine the density $\left(\dfrac{M}{V}\right)$ of several of the objects listed above. Complete at least three trials with each object and record the data on a chart in your notebook.

B. Describe in your notebook each step you used in Procedure A.

C. On a graph, plot mass on the vertical axis and volume on the horizontal axis. Complete the calculations necessary to determine the density of each object.

INTERPRETATION

1. What do the relative densities of different substances indicate about either the number of atoms or the weight of the atoms found in the same volume of each substance?

PROBLEMS

The term *specific gravity* is sometimes used to compare the weight of a substance with the weight of an equal volume of water. By definition:

$$\text{specific gravity} = \frac{\text{weight of any volume of a substance}}{\text{weight of an equal volume of water}}$$

Since density is a measure of the weight of a given volume of a substance, we can define specific gravity in this way:

$$\text{specific gravity} = \frac{\text{density of the substance}}{\text{density of water}}$$

For example, 10 ml of mercury weighs 136 grams. We already have found that 10 ml of water weighs 10 grams. Then the specific gravity of mercury can be determined by using either of the above equations:

$$\text{specific gravity of mercury} = \frac{136 \text{ grams}}{10 \text{ grams}} = 13.6$$

or

$$\text{specific gravity of mercury} = \frac{136 \text{ grams per 10 ml}}{10 \text{ grams per 10 ml}} = 13.6$$

Note that the same units (grams or grams per ml) appear in both the numerator and denominator of the two fractions. When we divide anything by itself, we get 1 as the quotient. Therefore, specific gravity is a number, but a number with no units. It simply indicates how many times heavier a substance is than the weight of an equal volume of water. When we say that the specific gravity of mercury is 13.6, we mean that any amount of mercury is 13.6 times as heavy as the same amount of water.

Figure 7 · 11.
Is the density of the iceberg greater or less than that of the water?

1. Fifty ml of concentrated sulfuric acid was found to weigh 92 grams. What is the specific gravity of this substance?
2. If 1 cubic foot of sea water weighs 64 pounds and 1 cubic foot of pure water weighs 62.4 pounds, what is the specific gravity of sea water?
3. If 1 liter (1000 ml) of gasoline weighs 670 grams, what is the specific gravity of gasoline?
4. If the specific gravity of ebony wood is 1.2, what will a cubic foot of the wood weigh (see Problem 2)?
5. The density of methyl alcohol is about 0.8 grams per milliliter. What is its specific gravity? Would ten milliliters of methyl alcohol be heavier than or lighter than ten milliliters of water?

Measurement of Time

Man has been measuring time since at least 4236 B.C., the date of the earliest known calendar. It is likely that people who lived much earlier than this also had ways of measuring time. And it is certain that modern man attaches much importance to the measurement of time. You can get an idea of how important such measurement is today by recording the number of calendars and clocks you see in one day!

Why should man be so concerned about measuring time? One answer to this question is obvious: He needs to know when to perform certain actions. You, for example, must know when to leave home in the morning to arrive at school on time, what time to be in the gym for basketball practice, and what time to be ready for a date.

Unless someone invents a time machine that will "unwind" history, we can only guess at the reasons Cro-Magnon man might have wished to time his actions. But we know that he hunted herd animals, such as reindeer, which migrated at certain times of the year. We can therefore imagine he wanted to know the timing of these migrations so that he could stay with the herds he hunted.

Though we are not sure how important the measurement of time was to Cro-Magnon hunters, we can be certain that it was often a matter of life or death to some of the earliest crop-raising people. Included among them were people who farmed on the banks of the Nile River, in Northeast Africa. This location had many advantages for crop-raising, one of which was that the river flooded every year *at a regular time*. In so doing, it irrigated the fields of the early Egyptian farmers. But the crops had to be ready to benefit from the floods, so the farmers had to know exactly when the river would rise. It is perhaps for this reason that the Egyptians developed the earliest known calendar.

A few miles southwest of London, England, there is a group of large stones—some.weighing several tons—arranged in a curious pattern. The stones at this site (Stonehenge) are believed to have been installed about 3500 years ago by a farming people. So far, no one has proved beyond doubt just what purpose Stonehenge served for these people. But some scientists have shown that they *could* have been used to calculate the time of year. Stonehenge has been measured and mapped in great detail. One scientist has recently shown that the time of year can be accurately determined by lining up the positions of sunrise and sunset with some of the large stones. Since we know that farmers need information about the time of year—when to plant, when to harvest, and so forth—this explanation of Stonehenge seems reasonable.

Doubleday & Company

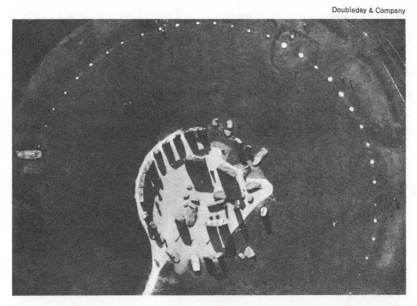

Figure 7 · 12.
Stonehenge
(aerial view).

John R. Brownlie from Photo Researchers

Figure 7 · 13.
Stonehenge
(ground view).

Since the days of the early Nile farmers and the Stonehenge people, man has devised ever more complex ways of making a living. And his need to know when to perform certain actions has grown increasingly important. As you know, nearly everyone in today's industrial world measures time. To understand why such measurements are important in our society, we need only imagine the problems that might arise in a factory or office if everyone arrived for work at a different time. Timing is important when events require the coöperation of many people from different places.

We have mentioned only in passing two methods of measuring time: calendars and clocks. The calendar is used to measure large units of time, such as days, months, and years. As you know, it was probably first invented by the Egyptians. But other agricultural peoples—for instance, the Maya of Central America—also invented calendars. This is not surprising in view of the need for accurately timing agricultural events (planting, and so forth) and

Figure 7 · 14. Early timing devices. (A) Water clock. (B) Hourglass. (C) Burning rope. (D) Sundial. Try to explain how each of these devices worked. What disadvantages do you see in using each method?

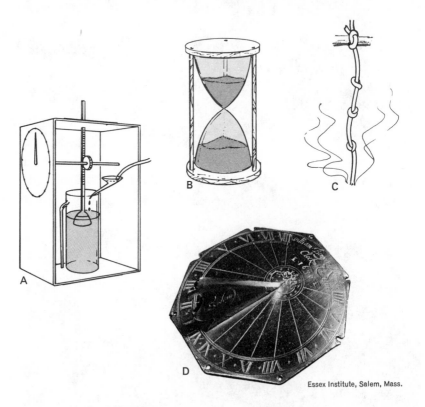

the fact that agriculture was independently developed by various peoples.

Clocks are used to measure small units of time, such as hours, minutes, and seconds. Sundials, one of the first clocks, originated in Babylonia before 2000 B.C. They were useless at night and on cloudy days. Because they were dependent on the sun, sundials were eventually replaced by more useful timepieces.

In the Orient, one of the earliest timing devices was a knotted rope. The rope was lit at one end, and the unit of time was the period required for the fire to travel from one knot to another.

Later devices for measuring time included the water clock and the hourglass. They served to measure fairly large units of time, so they were called *hour tellers*. The most accurate of the hour tellers was the water clock, which was improved by the addition of a simple dial to mark the hour (Figure 7 · 14). In 1617 a pendulum-regulated clock that accurately measured small units of time was invented. Today, there are timepieces, such as quartz clocks and atomic clocks, that are able to measure small units of time with great precision.

Precise measurement of time will be a key requirement in many of the investigations to follow.

INVESTIGATION 21: Inventing a Simple Timing Device

We usually have little problem telling time; modern watches and clocks are dependable and available almost anywhere. During this investigation you are asked to assume that we are living just before the time of Galileo. So you have no clocks or watches. Yet we need a way to measure short lengths of time. To do so, we must have short and equal *units* of time.

MATERIALS

   To be provided.

PROCEDURES

A. Each team is to invent some kind of simple timing device using only the materials available in the room. The device must be suitable for measuring events that begin and end within a rather short period of time. Once your timer is complete, proceed with Procedure B.

B. Use your timer to time different events—such as how long it takes for different students to walk the length of a room, or how long it takes to copy each word in this paragraph on a piece of paper. Think of other events that can be timed. You may express the time in clicks, marks, volume, or any unit your timing device provides.

INTERPRETATION

1. Prepare a brief report on your method of timing, and describe the events you timed. For example, suppose your timer consisted of tapping a pencil lightly on the table or desk at regular intervals. Your unit of time would then be a pencil tap instead of a second or minute.

REFERENCES

Asimov, Isaac. *Realm of Measure.* New York: Houghton Mifflin Co., 1960.

Bell, Thelma Harrington, and Bell, Corydon. *The Riddle of Time.* New York: Viking Press, Inc., 1963.

Fox, Russell. *The Science of Science.* New York: Walker & Co., 1963.

Hogben, Lancelot. *Wonderful World of Mathematics.* Garden City, N.Y.: Garden City Books, 1955.

Lehrman, R. L., and Scwartz, C. *Foundations of Physics.* New York: Holt, Rinehart & Winston, Inc., 1965.

Moulton, Ray, and Schifferes. *Autobiography of Science.* Garden City, N.Y.: Doubleday & Co., Inc., 1953.

Analysis of Motion

Early in this course you read about Aristotle, one of the greatest Greek philosophers and teachers. He wrote and lectured widely on astronomy, biology, physics, medicine, philosophy, and other subjects in which he was interested. Aristotle's opinions on nearly every subject were highly respected, and his writings affected European thought for hundreds of years.

Aristotle suggested that all matter is composed of only four elements—Earth, Air, Water, and Fire. According to this concept, most solids, such as soil or rocks, are composed chiefly of the element Earth. Steam is produced by combining the two elements Fire (heat) and Water. Aristotle also believed that each of the four elements has a natural position relative to the others. Earth, the heaviest, has the lowest position. Above Earth is Water, then Air, and finally the lightest, Fire. Each of these elements, if moved from its natural position, seeks to return to that position. Thus Earth falls through Air and Water. Water falls through Air. Fire rises through the other three.

Most substances were thought to be mixtures of two or more of these elements. Each substance tends to move upward or downward, depending upon the proportions of elements within the substance. If this theory seems silly, consider the following question: Why does smoke rise upward through Air? Followers of Aristotle would have said that smoke is a mixture of Fire and Air (with a little Earth and perhaps a little Water), but largely Fire. The natural place of Fire is above Earth, Water, and Air. Since there is more Fire than other elements in smoke, the desire of Fire to rise to its natural position is greater than the desire of the other elements. So smoke rises. Some of the element Earth, in the form of ashes, may break away from the smoke and follow its own desire to fall to the ground—its natural place.

It is difficult to argue against this kind of explanation (remember the demons). Evidence that contradicts the theory is just as difficult to collect as is supporting evidence. Aristotle attempted to provide a *reason* for the tendency of various substances to move upward or downward. One of the questions he was attempting to answer is "Why do objects fall?" We may laugh at his explanation. To say that a rock falls to the earth because its natural position is below that of Fire, Air, and Water seems strange to us. But we have no adequate answer to the question, even today. You may say that objects fall because of gravity. But what is gravity? Aristotle might say it is the desire of an object to seek the earth! Neither "gravity" nor "desire" gives us a real explanation.

Aristotle dealt with two kinds of motion in his writings. He considered the motion of falling bodies, the rising of water from springs, the rising of smoke in the air, and so forth, to be *natural motion*. Motion in such cases is caused by the natural tendency of each element to seek its natural position. But a rock that is thrown into the air moves upward and then horizontally; natural motion does not explain this. Therefore, he called the motion of a thrown object *forced motion*. He suggested a model to explain forced motion. According to this model, air, which is pushed aside by the moving object, rushes around behind the object and pushes it forward. Thus such moving objects continue to move only because there is a continuous push on them.

Aristotle suggested that heavy objects fall at greater speeds than do light objects. Earlier scholars had also stated that the speed of fall is proportional to weight—that is, a ten-pound object falls ten times as fast as a one-pound object. Though a few writers state that their observations contradicted this, the hypothesis was accepted by most people until the time of Galileo.

Almost 2000 years after Aristotle, Galileo (1564–1642) studied the problem of motion. Galileo suggested that one must observe objects in motion, measure their speeds, compare their weights, and so forth, in order to understand motion. Galileo's insistence on careful observation and the need for experiments did much to change man's approach to problems of science. His writings had tremendous effect on scientists for the next few centuries.

INVESTIGATION 22: Falling Objects

We cannot be sure just what evidence Aristotle and Galileo used to arrive at their theories about falling objects. Galileo lived about 2000 years after Aristotle, and we might expect that he benefited from some of the work done in intervening years. You will be performing this investigation about 350 years after Galileo completed his work. Later you will investigate falling objects in greater detail and take advantage of some of the ideas and equipment developed since the time of Galileo.

In this investigation you will use simple equipment to test Aristotle's theory that the rate of fall is proportional to weight—in other words, the heavier an object is, the faster it will fall. From your work, you should be able to form a judgment about Aristotle's theory.

MATERIALS (per class)
   Sheets of paper of uniform size
   Several staplers

PROCEDURES

Figure 8 · 1A.
Folding and
stapling a single
sheet of paper.

A. Fold a sheet of paper in half. Fold the paper in half again. Staple the four layers of paper together at the open corner (Figure 8 · 1A).

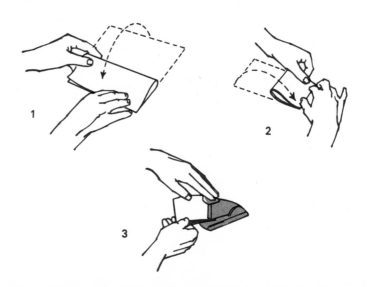

B. Repeat Procedure A, using two sheets of paper (Figure 8 • 1*B*).

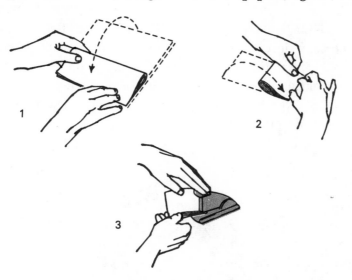

Figure 8 · 1*B*.
Folding and
stapling two
sheets of paper.

C. Repeat Procedure A, using four sheets of paper (Figure 8 • 1*C*).

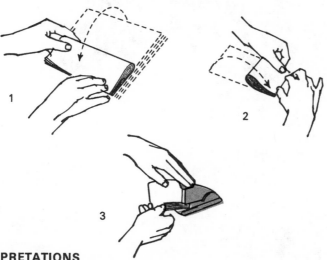

Figure 8 · 1*C*.
Folding and
stapling four
sheets of paper.

INTERPRETATIONS

1. According to Aristotle's theory, which of the folded papers should fall most rapidly?
2. Which of the papers do *you* think will fall most rapidly? If your answer is different from your answer in Interpretation 1, give your reason for the difference.

PROCEDURES (continued)

D. Hold the single folded sheet in one hand and the four folded sheets in the other, as shown in Figure 8 · 2. Release both at the same instant and determine the approximate difference, if any, in the time required for each to fall to the floor. Repeat several times. Record observations in your notebook.

E. Repeat Procedure D, using two folded sheets and four folded sheets. Record observations.

H/W Photographics

Figure 8 · 2. Carrying out Procedure D.

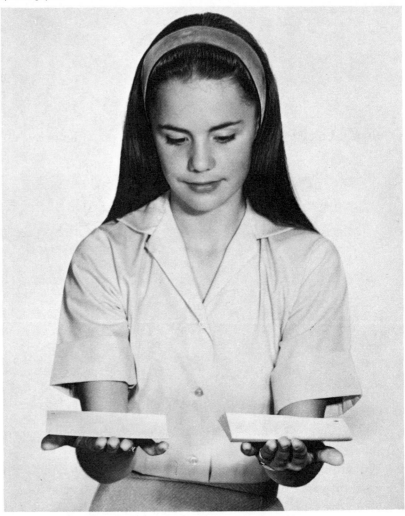

INTERPRETATIONS (continued)

3. Compare the results with the prediction you made in Interpretation 2. Make a general statement for falling objects based on your observations in this investigation.

PROCEDURES (continued)

F. To determine whether the size of an object influences its rate of fall, fold the single sheet of paper in half two more times (for a total of four folds) and staple the open side. Then compare the rates of fall of this sheet and the four sheets prepared in Procedure C.

INTERPRETATIONS (continued)

4. Does size influence the rate at which objects fall? Does weight influence the rate at which objects fall? Do light objects fall faster than heavy objects? Record your answers in the form of complete sentences.
5. Does your interpretation of Procedure F change the statement you made about rate of fall in Interpretation 3? If so, revise the statement. If not, why do you think your original explanation is still correct?

Motion and Rest

We know from experience that some kind of push is needed to make an object move. If the object is left alone, it stays at rest. It would *appear* that the natural condition of objects is rest, and that motion is achieved only with a push or a pull.

INVESTIGATION 23: The Natural Condition of an Object

Is rest the natural condition of an object? What are some of the things that affect objects in motion and objects at rest? What kinds of measurements need to be made in a study of motion? This investigation should help you find the answers to some of these questions.

MATERIALS (per team)
   Grooved track and force mechanism (Figure 8 · 3)
   Steel ball or marble (to fit groove)

Figure 8 · 3.

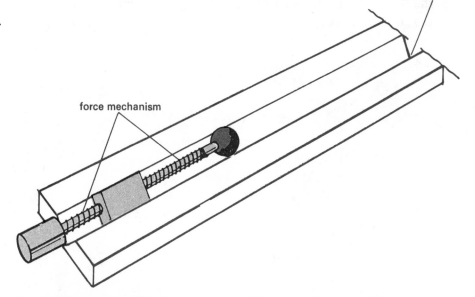

PROCEDURES

A. Place the grooved track on a level surface. Gently shoot a marble or steel ball along the groove. Observe and describe its motion. Does it come to rest, or does it keep moving?

B. Change the position of the track so that the ball must roll uphill. Shoot the ball and observe its motion. Change the position of the track so that the ball must roll downhill. Repeat the procedure. Record your observations.

INTERPRETATIONS

1. Imagine that the track is very long and straight. If the slope is downhill, would you expect the angle of slope to affect the amount of time the ball will continue to roll? If so, how?
2. If the slope of the same track is uphill, would you expect the angle of slope to influence the amount of time the ball will continue to roll? If so, how?
3. What causes the ball to act as it does when the track is level?
4. What will happen if the ball is rolled with the same force along a level track that is smoother? along a level track that is rougher?
5. If no forces act on the ball after the first push, what will happen to the motion of the ball? Why?
6. In your own words state a theory that might explain the natural condition of an object.
7. What are some of the factors that could affect the motion of an object?
8. What measurements must be made before the speed of a moving object can be expressed in numbers?

INVESTIGATION 24: Speed

The term *speed* is part of your everyday vocabulary. We talk about the speed of automobiles, jet airplanes, and even the speed of sound and of light. This investigation is designed to show you a method of measuring speed.

MATERIALS (per team)
   Grooved speed-track system (Figure 8·4)
   Steel ball about ½ inch in diameter
   Timer
   Graph paper

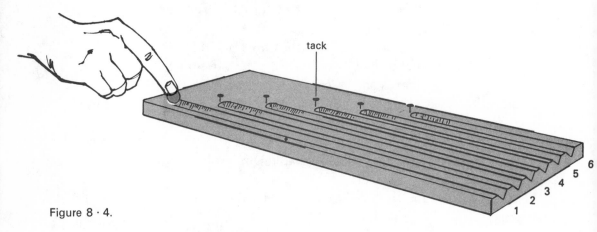

tack

Figure 8 · 4.

PROCEDURES
A. Hold the steel ball against the starting post in Track 1. Release the ball, and determine the time it takes the ball to reach the end of the track. Time can be measured with a click timer, with a stop watch, or by careful observation of a sweep second hand on a watch or clock. Teamwork is important! It is best to make several trials, and calculate the *average* time for all trials.
B. Repeat the procedure, using Tracks 2 through 6. Record the average time for each track.
C. Measure the length of each track in centimeters or inches.
D. Plot the data on a bar graph, using the horizontal axis to show distance traveled and the vertical axis to show time.

INTERPRETATIONS

1. Compare your graph with the appearance of the speed track system. Describe similarities and differences, and suggest an explanation.
2. Assume that s = speed, d = distance, and t = time. Explain each of the following equations:

    a. $s = \dfrac{d}{t}$ b. $d = st$ c. $t = \dfrac{d}{s}$

3. Suggest ways in which the design of this investigation could be improved to yield more accurate results.
4. In your own words write out a definition of speed.

Understanding Force

Force was used by man long before he realized what it was. He applied force when he lifted a stone or threw a spear. Today we use many devices to produce force: jet engines, electric motors, gasoline-powered engines, and atomic energy reactors. We have talked about the attractive forces between atoms and between molecules, and we have seen in Investigation 22 that there is a force called gravity.

All of these examples involve lifting, pushing, pulling, or attracting. Force is any influence that tends to cause matter to move. The word *tends* is important. For example, if you attempt to lift one end of an automobile you are exerting force, even though the car is too heavy to lift. Or, if you lean against a solid wall you exert force, even though the wall does not move.

It takes force to compress, stretch, or bend a spring. The atoms in a spring are arranged in a particular way. To bend them out of their pattern requires that the electrons holding them together be crowded in some places and thinned out in others. Where the electrons are crowded together, they repel each other more strongly and give the metal spring a tendency to return to its original shape. The more you bend the material out of its normal shape, the more crowded the electrons become and the greater is the tendency of the material to return to its original shape. One way to measure this tendency is to observe the effect of a spring on a steel ball.

INVESTIGATION 25: Force and Bending

MATERIALS (per team)
Ruler
Grooved track and force mechanism (Figure 8 · 3)
Steel ball or marble
Timer
Graph paper

PROCEDURES
A. Measure the length of the track. Using the setting of least spring tension, launch the steel ball or marble and measure the time required for the ball to travel the length of the track. Repeat several times, and determine the average speed.
B. Launch the steel ball, using a setting of greater spring tension on the force mechanism. Calculate the average speed from several trials.
C. Continue investigating the relationship between spring tension and the speed of the ball, using other settings on the force mechanism. Plot your data on a graph, showing speed on the vertical axis and force (represented by the different positions of the shooter) on the horizontal axis.
D. Beginning with the setting used in Procedure A, measure the distance from the spring to its point of contact with the ball for each setting on the force mechanism.

INTERPRETATION
1. Using your data, can you make any statement about a relationship between the bending of the spring and the speed of the steel ball?

INVESTIGATION 26: Force and Stretching

MATERIALS (per team)

    Force gauge (Figure 8 · 5)

    Masking tape

    6 to 8 identical objects (marbles, ball bearings, nails, screws, or other objects of convenient size and weight)

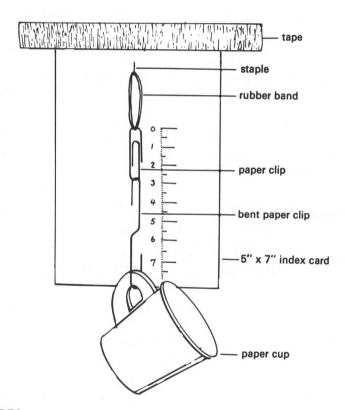

Figure 8 · 5.
Set-up for
Procedures A–E.

tape

staple

rubber band

paper clip

bent paper clip

5" x 7" index card

paper cup

PROCEDURES

A. Tape the force gauge to the edge of a table or desk so that the rubber band, paper clips, and cup hang down along the scale on the card.

B. Read the position of the lower end of the rubber band on the scale. Be sure that your eye is level with the end of the rubber band when you take the reading.

C. In your notebook prepare a chart similar to the one shown in Figure 8 · 6. Include numbers for 4, 5, and 6 objects.

Figure 8 · 6.

Number of Objects	Scale Reading	Change in Scale Reading
0 1 2 3		

D. Put one object in the cup, and record the scale reading. Add identical objects, one at a time and record the scale reading each time.

E. Remove all objects from the cup, and check to see that the scale reading is the same as it was when you began. If it has changed you will need to repeat Procedure D.

INTERPRETATIONS

1. Calculate the change in the length of the rubber band caused by each additional object. Record these changes in the third column on your chart. Look for a pattern in the changes.
   a. What is the pattern?
   b. What explanation can you give for the pattern?
   c. How might you explain any irregularities in the pattern?
2. Use your model of the structure of matter to explain the data.

INVESTIGATION 27: Friction

Friction is the resistance an object experiences as it moves on or through another. You probably are familiar with friction. You may have used the effect of friction to warm your hands by rubbing them together. Space vehicles returning to earth depend on the friction of air to slow them down. The movement of a solid body over another surface is resisted by a force called friction. The movement of an object through fluids such as air and water is resisted by friction.

What factors affect frictional forces? How are these factors related to the structure of matter? These questions are of great theoretical and practical importance. They are important in building our understanding of the structure of matter. They are of practical importance because our society depends on transportation, and the control of friction is one of the biggest problems in transportation.

MATERIALS (per team)

  Force gauge (used in Investigation 26)
  3 wooden blocks (Figure 8·7)
  Sheet of sandpaper
  Pane of glass
  2 pieces of glass tubing or rods (4-inch lengths)
  2 rubber bands
  Masking tape

PROCEDURES

In Procedures A through E you are asked to determine (1) whether the *shape* of surfaces in contact (smooth, rough, and curved) affects the amount of friction between objects, and (2) whether the *area*, or size, of surfaces in contact affects the amount of friction between objects.

A. Lay the force gauge on the desk or table, and straighten out the rubber band and paper clips. The free end of the second clip should extend beyond the edge of the gauge. Pick up the free end and hold it so that the rubber band is straight but not stretched. Record the scale reading (at the end of the rubber band).

B. Number the blocks as shown in Figure 8 · 7. Place Block 1 on the sandpaper, with one of the large sides down. Attach the free end of the force gauge to the hook on the block (Figure 8 · 7). Pull on the force gauge so that the block slides at a steady speed over the sandpaper. Take a reading on the force gauge scale. Record the reading.

C. Place the block on the pane of glass (same side down). Pull on the force gauge so that the block slides at a steady speed. Record the reading on the force gauge scale.

Figure 8 · 7.
Force gauge and
wooden blocks
to be used in
Procedures A–K.

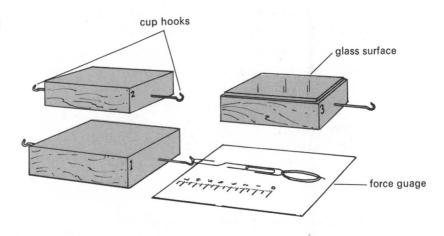

cup hooks

glass surface

force guage

INTERPRETATIONS

1. Glass is made from melted sand. How can you explain the difference between the force required to pull wood over sandpaper and the force required to pull wood over glass?

2. How can this difference in force be related to the structure of matter?

PROCEDURES (continued)

D. Turn Block 1 so that one of its smaller sides is down. Do you think it will require more, less, or the same amount of force to pull the block in this position as compared with the force required in Procedure C? Write down your prediction. Now test your prediction by pulling the block over the glass. Pull on the force gauge so that the block slides with a steady speed. Record the reading.

INTERPRETATIONS (continued)

3. Is the amount of friction between objects related to the area of the surfaces in contact?

PROCEDURES (continued)

E. Lay two glass rods or tubes parallel to each other (about one inch apart) on the pane of glass. Put Block 1 on top of them and pull it with the force gauge so that it rolls with a steady speed. Record the reading.

INTERPRETATIONS (continued)

4. Make a sketch showing the motion of particles of wood and glass in Procedure D. Make another sketch showing the motion of particles of wood and glass in Procedure E.

PROCEDURES (continued)

In Procedures F through I you are asked to determine whether the *kind of material* that makes up the surfaces in contact affects the amount of friction.

F. Place Block 3—glass side down—on the pane of glass. Measure the force required to slide the block at a steady speed across the plate of glass. Record the reading on the scale.

G. Turn the block over so the glass surface is up. Use the force gauge to pull the block at a steady speed on the glass plate. Record the reading of the force gauge.

H. Put two rubber bands around Block 3 as shown in Figure 8 · 8. Be sure the rubber bands are not twisted. With the rubber bands acting as runners, pull the gauge so that the block moves at a steady speed over the glass. Record the reading.

INTERPRETATIONS (continued)

5. List several properties of rubber that you think make it useful for vehicle tires.

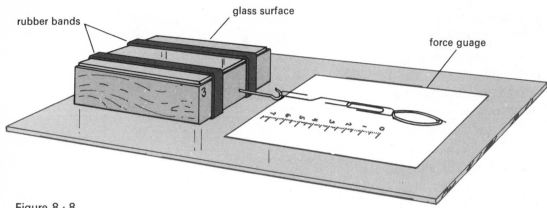

Figure 8 · 8.
Set-up for
Procedure H.

PROCEDURES (continued)

I. Remove the rubber bands and replace them with two pieces
of masking tape as shown in Figure 8 • 9. Be sure the sticky
side of the tape is out. Try to pull the block over the glass at
a steady speed with the gauge. Record your observations.

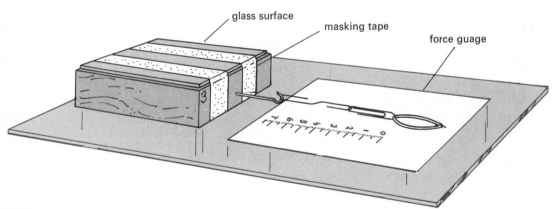

Figure 8 · 9.
Set-up for
Procedure I.

INTERPRETATIONS (continued)

6. Explain the result of Procedure I in terms of the behavior of
the particles that make up the surface of masking tape. You
will want to take into account both the shape (roughness) of
the surface and the type of material involved.

PROCEDURES (continued)

In Procedures J and K you will investigate the effect of weight on friction.

J. Prepare a chart similar to the one shown in Figure 8 · 10. Use your force gauge to measure the force needed to pull Block 1 at a steady speed on a smooth level surface, such as a counter top. Repeat, using Blocks 1 and 2 hooked together, one behind the other. Record the reading. Repeat, using all three blocks hooked together, in single file.

Figure 8 · 10.

Blocks		Scale Reading
	1	
Hooked together	1 and 2	
	1, 2, and 3	
Stacked	1 and 2	
	1, 2, and 3	

K. Unhook the second and third blocks. Place Block 2 *on top of* Block 1. Pull the two blocks over the same surface used in Procedure J, and record the reading. Then stack the third block on top of the others. Pull the three blocks and record data on the chart.

INTERPRETATIONS (continued)

7. Does the amount of friction depend on the area of the surfaces in contact? Does it depend on weight?

A Dialogue on Friction

Friction, like other natural phenomena, might be explained in terms of demons. Before you dismiss this idea completely, imagine that you and a neighbor called Faustus are discussing the matter. Faustus, who believes in the demon theory, begins by asking "How do you know that it is friction that brings a rolling ball to a stop and not demons?"

YOU. I don't believe in demons.

FAUSTUS. I do.

YOU. Anyway, I don't see how demons can make friction.

FAUSTUS. They just stand in front of things and push to stop them from moving.

YOU. I can't see any demons even on the roughest table.

FAUSTUS. They are too small, also transparent.

Y. But there is more friction on rough surfaces.

F. More demons.

Y. Oil helps.

F. Oil drowns demons.

Y. If I polish the table, there is less friction and the ball rolls farther.

F. You are wiping the demons off; there are fewer to push.

Y. A heavier ball experiences more friction.

F. More demons push it; and it crushes their bones more.

Y. If I put a rough brick on the table I can push against friction with more and more force, up to a limit, and the block stays still, with friction just balancing my push.

F. Of course, the demons push just hard enough to stop you moving the brick; but there is a limit to their strength beyond which they collapse.

Y. But when I push hard enough and get the brick moving there is friction that drags the brick as it moves along.

F. Yes, once they have collapsed the demons are crushed by the brick. It is their crackling bones that oppose the sliding.[1]

Y. I cannot feel them.

F. Rub your finger along the table.

Y. Friction follows definite laws. For example, experiment shows that a brick sliding along the table is dragged by friction with a force independent of velocity.

F. Of course, same number of demons to crush, however fast you run over them.

---

[1]If Faustus has the equipment he should offer you a microphone attached to a glass table, with connections to an amplifier and loudspeaker. Then if you roll a steel ball along the table you will indeed hear noises like crushing demons.

Y. If I slide a brick along the table again and again, the friction is the same each time. Demons would be crushed in the first trip.

F. Yes, but they multiply incredibly fast.

Y. There are other laws of friction; for example, the drag is proportional to the pressure holding the surfaces together.

F. The demons live in the pores of the surface; more pressure makes more of them rush out to push and be crushed. Demons act in just the right way to push and drag with the forces you find in your experiments.

By this time, Faustus' game is clear. Whatever properties you ascribe to friction he will claim, in some form, for demons. At first his demons appear arbitrary and unreliable; but when you produce regular laws of friction he produces a regular sociology of demons. At that point there is a deadlock, with demons and friction serving as alternative names for a set of properties—and each debater is back to his first remark.[2]

FOR FURTHER DISCUSSION

1. Who do you think presented the best explanation for friction —you or Faustus? Why?

2. Develop arguments for the existence of demons by comparing the behavior of a block sliding on sandpaper and the behavior of the same block sliding on glass. Use the same examples to develop arguments *against* demons.

[2]Eric M. Rogers, *Physics for the Inquiring Mind.* Princeton, N. J.: Princeton University Press, 1960) pp. 343–345. Used by permission of the publisher.

The Force of Gravity

Until the time of Isaac Newton (1642–1727) men generally believed that the sun, moon, and stars behave according to rules of motion that are different from the rules of motion on earth. They believed that heavenly objects are circular in shape, move in circles, and (with the exception of planets) have moved through the same circular pattern since the beginning of time. By assuming that each planet moves on a circle which rolls on another circle, early astronomers were able to account for the apparent ability of planets to "wander among the stars."

All this was a logical extension of their model, which separated the heavens from the earth and assumed that each has its own unique rules for the behavior of matter. Today we know that Earth is just one more body among the billions scattered through the universe. And we believe our planet and everything on it behave according to the same rules that apply elsewhere.

Man's desire to fit the movements of planets into the old model led to careful observations—which, oddly enough, eventually brought about the downfall of the old model. Newton examined the data collected from these observations. He decided that the movements of the planets could result from the same kind of force that causes objects to fall downward on earth. To convince other people of this hypothesis, he needed to provide some kind of proof that his model was more valid than the one people had accepted for thousands of years. He developed a new kind of mathematics, called *calculus*, and used it to show that only a force such as the one he described could account for the paths of the planets. This force was, of course, gravity.

Newton's statement of the law of gravity and other laws of motion was so complete that it explained many other things which had puzzled astronomers. He also made predictions about the shape of the earth, and described the conditions necessary for an artificial satellite to orbit the earth. Some of his predictions were so precise that we have been able to test them only recently, by observation from satellites. Newton's explanation of the motion of falling objects (which includes planets, stars, and moons) is an outstanding example of a successful model. His model has been tested by experiments, and it can be used to make many useful predictions about the movements of objects anywhere. You will not be asked to investigate all of the problems Newton solved. On the other hand, you will not simply memorize his formulas. In Investigation 23 you were asked to describe a characteristic of objects that Newton called *inertia*. The next investigation has been designed so that you can gather information about the way objects respond to the force called *gravity*.

INVESTIGATION 28: Motion and the Force of Gravity

MATERIALS (per team)
   Force gauge (same as in Investigation 26)
   Marble
   Steel ball
   2 grooved tracks
   Block of wood
   Timer
   Meterstick

PROCEDURES
A. Using the force gauge, measure the force with which gravity pulls on the marble and on the steel ball. Record your observations carefully.

INTERPRETATIONS
1. How many times heavier than the marble is the steel ball? (Divide the change in the length of the rubber band resulting from the force of gravity on the steel ball by the change resulting from the force of gravity on the marble.)
2. Would you predict that the speed of the steel ball will change more rapidly than that of the marble if the two are falling?

PROCEDURES (continued)
B. Set up the tracks as shown in Figure 8·11. Mark a starting

point at the upper end of the sloping track. Hold the end of a pencil in the groove at this point, and place the marble against it. Release the marble by lifting the pencil, and measure the time required for the marble to roll *the length of the level track.*

ratio — $\frac{5}{1}$ — to — 100 —

Figure 8 · 11. Set-up for Procedures B–E. A 5/100 ratio means that the track is raised 1 cm for every 20 cm of its length.

INTERPRETATIONS (continued)

3. Calculate the average speed of the marble on the level track.

PROCEDURES (continued)

C. Repeat Procedure B using the steel ball in place of the marble.

INTERPRETATIONS (continued)

4. Calculate the average speed of the steel ball on the level track.
5. How do the results of Interpretations 3 and 4 compare with your prediction in Interpretation 2?

PROCEDURES (continued)

D. Use the timer to find how long it takes the marble to change its speed from zero (at release) to the average speed it had on the level track.
E. Repeat Procedure D using the steel ball in place of the marble.

INTERPRETATIONS (continued)

6. *Acceleration* is any change in speed. (A decrease in speed is negative acceleration and is usually called *deceleration*.) To measure acceleration—that is, how rapidly speed is changed— we must know the speed at the beginning and at the end of the trial and the period of time involved. We can express this as a formula:

$$\text{acceleration} = \frac{\text{change in speed}}{\text{time to produce the change}}$$

or

$$\text{acceleration} = \frac{\text{final speed minus initial speed}}{\text{the amount of time the speed was changing}}$$

Calculate the acceleration of the steel ball and the acceleration of the marble.

Acceleration

If you stop a bicycle at the top of a hill and then start coasting down the hill, you will experience a constant increase in speed. This might make you want to slow down by using the brakes. When you are on the hill gravity can cause your speed to increase or decrease; friction can cause it to decrease.

A ball rolled up a hill does not move at a steady speed and then suddenly stop. It will gradually slow down, stop, and then start rolling back down the hill. Lacking brakes, the ball will continue increasing in speed until it reaches the bottom or until something stops it.

It is difficult to determine the speed of a ball rolling down a hill at any *one instant* of time. In the next investigation you will attempt to determine the average speed of a ball for different intervals of time, while it is on the slope. From these averages you can determine the acceleration of the ball.

INVESTIGATION 29: Measuring Acceleration

Study the directions carefully before beginning the investigation. Your results can be accurate only if each person on your team does his job carefully.

MATERIALS (per team)
   Track
   Marking guide (card with a small hole in it)
   Masking tape
   Strip of paper (as long as the track)
   Steel ball or marble
   Timer
   Metric ruler
   Graph paper

PROCEDURES
A. Set the track at a slope of about 5/100 (Figure 8·12).

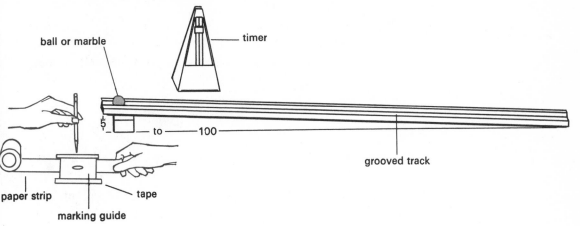

ball or marble

timer

to ——— 100

grooved track

paper strip

tape

marking guide

Figure 8 · 12. Set-up for Procedures A–F.

B. Tape the marking guide to the table near the raised end of the track, as shown in Figure 8 · 12. Slide the strip of paper under the marking guide.

C. Have one member of your team put the ball at the top of the track and hold it in position with a pencil. Have another team member grasp the end of the strip of paper and move it until it is even with the ball. Start the timer and release the ball at the instant the timer clicks. Practice sliding the strip of paper along the table so that its end stays even with the ball rolling down the track.

D. Now have another team member practice marking the moving paper strip through the hole in the marking guide. Use a ball-point pen, and practice tapping the strip in time with each click of the timer.

E. When you have practiced enough to make your results dependable, turn over the paper strip and move it into starting position. Have the marker begin tapping the paper through the hole in time with the clicks. This will mark the beginning point for your record. When the ball is released and the strip of paper is pulled, the marks on the paper will be separated by the distance the ball has moved between clicks.

F. Measure and record the distances between marks.

INTERPRETATIONS

1. Since the time interval for each distance you measured is one click, the average speed for that interval is numerically equal to the distance.

$$\text{average speed} = \frac{\text{distance between marks}}{1 \text{ click}}$$

    In your notebook record the average speed for each time interval carefully.

2. Prepare a graph of your data. Plot the average speeds on the vertical axis and the time intervals on the horizontal axis.

3. Study the graph. Does the speed increase by the same amount from one time interval to the next?

4. If the amount of change from one time interval to the next is relatively constant, what is the average change in speed per time interval? What is the acceleration?

5. Compare your graph with the graphs prepared by other teams. Describe and explain any similarities and differences.

6. If the slope was increased, what would be the effect on the acceleration?

INVESTIGATION 30: Mass

You have been told that an object in a capsule orbiting the earth is "weightless." This does not mean that such an object loses any of the matter it contains on Earth, where it has weight. All the atoms that are part of the object when it is on Earth are still there.

However, because the object is in orbit, it can no longer be weighed in the normal fashion. In fact, because of the rotation of the earth, an object has a different weight at the North Pole than it does at the equator. It is not the object that changes; it is the interaction between the object and the earth. There is something that is characteristic of the object no matter where it is; and that something we call *mass*. The mass of an object is a measure of the number and kinds of atoms that make it up. (Remember that an atom of gold has more protons, neutrons, and electrons in it than an atom of hydrogen.) Mass is what determines the resistance of

NASA

Figure 8 · 13. American astronaut Edward H. White, II performing his space walk. He is attached to the Gemini IV spacecraft by a 25-ft. umbilical cord. Does he have weight?

an object to changes of motion. And it is the number and kinds of atoms in the object that determines the degree of attraction between it and the earth. The distinction between mass and weight is that mass is a property of an object, while weight is a measure of the force with which the earth attracts the object. A few million miles away from the earth the weight of any object would be almost zero, but its mass would remain constant.

When we determine the mass of an object, we also have a measure of its resistance to change in its state of motion, because both of these properties depend on the number and kinds of atoms present in the object.

MATERIALS (per team)
    Track with force mechanism
    Timer
    Steel ball
    Marble (about the size of the steel ball)

PROCEDURES

A. In your notebook, copy the table shown in Figure 8 · 14. Place the track in a horizontal position. Launch the marble and record the data called for in the table. Using the same setting for the shooter, complete two more trials with the marble and three trials with the steel ball.

Figure 8 · 14.

MARBLE				STEEL BALL			
Trial	Distance	Time	Speed	Trial	Distance	Time	Speed
1				1			
2				2			
3				3			
Average				Average			

B. Change the position of the track so that the marble and ball will be launched uphill. The slope must be steep enough to make the ball come to a stop before reaching the end of the track, when launched with the same force used in Procedure A. Measure the time required to bring the ball to a stop. Record the data in your notebook.

MARBLE				STEEL BALL				Figure 8 · 15.
Trial	Time	Change in speed	Accel-eration	Trial	Time	Change in speed	Accel-eration	
1				1				
2				2				
3				3				
Average				Average				

INTERPRETATIONS

1. Was there a noticeable difference between the average speed of the marble and the average speed of the steel ball in Procedure A?

2. What is the difference between the average acceleration of the marble and that of the steel ball in Procedure B? How might you explain this difference, using your model of the structure of matter?

REFERENCES

Andrade, Edward. *Physics for the Modern World.* New York: Barnes & Noble, Inc., 1963.

Brophy, James, and Paolucci, Henry. *Achievements of Galileo.* New Haven, Conn.: College and University Press, 1962.

Cohen, I. Bernard. *The Birth of a New Physics.* Garden City, N.Y.: Doubleday & Co., Inc. (Anchor Books), 1960.

Constant, Woodbridge F. *Fundamental Laws of Physics.* Reading, Mass.: Addison Wesley Publishing Co., 1963.

Gamow, George. "Gravity" *Scientific American* Reprint #273. San Francisco: W. H. Freeman and Co., March 1961.

———. *Gravity.* Garden City, N.Y.: Doubleday & Co., Inc. (Anchor Books), 1962.

Marcus, Rebecca B. *Galileo and Experimental Science.* New York: Franklin Watts, Inc., 1961.

PSSC. *Physics.* Boston: D.C. Heath & Co., 1965.

Victor, Edward. *Friction.* Chicago: Follett Publishing Co., 1961.

Motion and Energy

Cro-Magnon man must have observed many of the same forces and effects in nature that we see today. But what kind of model did he use to explain what he observed? We have no way of knowing, but we can guess that fear and superstition may have been the main ingredients of his thoughts and beliefs. Primitive man knew lightning, thunder, tornadoes, raging forest fires, earthquakes, and other natural phenomena. His own senses of fear and awe were probably the only basis he had for constructing models.

Just for convenience, imagine that Cro-Magnon man used the word *energy* to refer to the cause or power in natural events. He might then have classified energy according to the different events observed: wind energy, lightning energy, thunder energy, rain energy, sun energy, fire energy, and so forth. A modern model distinguishes between different kinds of energy—but not on the same basis supposedly used by our Cro-Magnon thinker.

We know that our surroundings are continuously changing. Our planet rotates on its axis as it moves around the sun. As a result, we have night and day. And because the earth's axis is "tilted," we have the changes known as seasons. Some days are clear and sunny. Others are cloudy and rainy. Sometimes the wind blows, and at other times it does not. Some days are hot. Others

Figure 9 · 1. Cro-Magnon men observing a tornado. What kind of model do you think these men might have used to explain this force of nature?

are cold. Most of these variables result from changes in kinds or amounts of energy. A modern model of energy takes into account our knowledge that all matter, from the largest star to the smallest particle of an atom, contains stored energy. Under certain conditions the energy may be released to bring about observable changes.

We have already used the term *energy* in referring to heat given off during certain chemical reactions. We have not yet explored the meaning of energy. Energy itself is not visible. But we can often observe the effects of energy on matter. As you investigate different kinds of energy, keep in mind that no matter how unlike their effects may be, different kinds of energy may be related. Cro-Magnon man probably saw no relationship between lightning and the warmth from his own fire. In what way do you think fire and lightning might be related?

Your energy comes from the food you eat. You might use some of this energy to roll a ball. What happens to the energy after you release the ball? The energy is transferred to the ball, and its effect can be observed as motion. But the amount of energy of motion can be determined only if you know the mass and speed of the ball. You will calculate energy of motion of some objects in this section.

In your investigations with bluestone, you changed heat energy into chemical energy. Energy can be changed from one form to another, but never created or destroyed. This concept is called the *Principle of Conservation of Energy.*

You will be asked to develop a model that will give you a better understanding of what *energy* really means. Use your own insight and prior knowledge, as well as the results of investigation, to develop the model. This does not mean that you will necessarily reach the goal, for it is a difficult one.

At this point we hope you will think carefully about the investigations you have performed and the models you have constructed. You should be prepared to relate these experiences to the investigations in the following sections.

Figure 9 · 2. What force could produce the amount of energy necessary to cause damage to the extent shown here?

UPI

PROBLEMS

1. List all the kinds of energy you think may exist (much as our imaginary Cro-Magnon man might have done in a more limited way).

2. Find out and report on possible causes of lightning and thunder and how the two are related.

3. Try to find historical accounts of tornadoes, typhoons, volcanic eruptions, and earthquakes. How have man's explanations of these natural events changed through history?

4. What scientific ideas are used in modern attempts to cause rainfall? What are some other examples of man's efforts to alter or control weather and climate?

The Meaning of Momentum

Momentum is a word that may be used to describe motion. Perhaps you know that a heavily loaded truck has more momentum than a sports car traveling at the same speed. A clear understanding of momentum will be useful in the study of motion and energy.

All moving objects have momentum, whether they are as large as the earth or as small as an atom. Studying the behavior of marbles may provide information that will be useful in improving your atomic model.

Objects have momentum only when they are in motion. Momentum is calculated by multiplying the mass of an object by the speed of the object.

$$M = mv$$
$$(M = \text{momentum}; m = \text{mass}; v = \text{speed})$$

(The v is taken from the word *velocity*, which has a meaning slightly different from that of *speed*. A definition of velocity includes both the speed and direction of motion. We will continue to use the term *speed*, however, because for our purposes it has much the same meaning as velocity.)

A cart weighing 20 grams and traveling at a constant speed of 5 centimeters per second has a momentum equal to the momentum of a 10 gram cart traveling at 10 centimeters per second.

Note that the momentum of the first cart is equal to the momentum of the second cart.

Cart 1: M = 20 grams x 5 cm/sec. = 100 gram centimeters/second

Cart 2: M = 10 grams x 10 cm/sec. = 100 gram centimeters/second

What would happen if a marble weighing 10 grams and traveling at a speed of 5 cm/second struck a 10 gram marble that was not moving? This and other problems dealing with momentum will be the focus of Investigation 31.

INVESTIGATION 31: Analysis of Momentum

MATERIALS (per team)
Track with force mechanism
8 marbles of the same weight
2 steel balls
Sheet of tracing paper
Sheet of carbon paper

PROCEDURES
A. Make sure the track is level. Place a marble in the groove about 5 cm from the launching point. Launch a second marble with a measured amount of force. Record the setting used on the force mechanism and the reaction that occurs between the 2 marbles.
B. Place 5 marbles in the middle of the grooved track so that they touch each other. Launch a marble with the same force setting used in Procedure A. Record the effect on the 5 marbles.
C. Place 5 marbles in the middle of the grooved track as in Procedure B. Shoot 2 marbles at the same time and with the same force setting used before. Record the effect on the 5 marbles. Repeat this procedure shooting 3 marbles at the same time, and record the effect on the other five.
D. Place a marble in the middle of the grooved track. Shoot one of the steel balls with the same force setting. Record your results.

INTERPRETATIONS
1. What happened to the momentum of the marbles launched in Procedures A, B, and C?
2. As a result of the collisions, how did the change in momentum of the steel ball in Procedure D compare with the change in momentum of the marbles that were launched in Procedures A, B, and C?

PROBLEMS
1. Carefully study the results of each procedure. Recall that momentum is a property of a moving object and is equal to the

mass of an object times its speed. From the results of the experiments you have performed, state a general law about momentum.

2. From your observations, predict what will happen if a steel ball is placed in the middle of the track and a marble is launched at it. Record your prediction.

PROCEDURES (continued)

E. Place a steel ball in the middle of the track, and launch a marble at it. Observe the direction of motion of each after the collision. Roughly compare the speed of the marble before and after the collision.

F. In previous procedures, the directions in which the marbles and steel balls moved after collision were limited by the track. In this procedure the steel balls will be free to move in any direction on a table top after they collide. Place the carbon paper on the table, carbon side up, and lay the tracing paper over it. The weight of each ball will leave a track on the bottom of the tracing paper. Roll the steel balls toward each other —one from each hand. Try to release the balls in such a way that they have approximately equal speed. Make sketches of several collisions, using circles to represent the steel balls and arrows to indicate their movements. Use ink to draw the circle and arrow for one ball. Use pencil to draw the circle and arrow for the other ball.

INTERPRETATIONS (continued)

3. What three factors seem to determine the results of the collisions you observed in Procedure E?

4. In the analysis of motion, it is not enough to know the speed of an object. You must also know the exact *direction* in which an object is moving. The combination of speed and direction is velocity. In Procedure F could you predict what direction each ball would take after the two collided?

As long as you limit the direction of motion with a track, it is fairly easy to predict the result of a collision. Without the track, the objects have greater freedom of movement, and the mathe-matics becomes complicated.

PROBLEMS (continued)

3. Suppose that an auto and a large, heavily-laden truck are each traveling at 50 miles per hour. Which would have the greatest change in direction and speed if they were to collide head-on? Base your answer on your previous investigation of the collision between a marble and a steel ball.

INVESTIGATION 32: Energy of Motion

You have seen that a rolling ball continues to move unless it is stopped by friction or by another object. The concept of momentum may be helpful in understanding motion, but it leaves some questions unanswered. For example, why is there a certain relationship between the number of marbles that strike a row of stationary marbles and the number that roll away?

During Investigation 29 you saw that the force of gravity can produce acceleration. But how is the change in speed related to gravity? When you lift a rock, gravity pulls down on it with a steady force. If you drop the rock from a height of six feet, it will be falling faster when it hits the ground than if you had dropped it from a height of only one foot. Every object has energy as a result of the pull of gravity. This energy is called energy of position, and it is changed into energy of motion if the object is allowed to fall.

Energy is stored up when you lift something, and is released as the object falls. If you could measure the speed of a falling object at different points in its path, you could compare the distance it has fallen with the speed it has gained. It is not easy to measure the speed of a falling object. A marble rolling in an inclined track may provide us with an opportunity to compare the change in height with the speed produced. Data from this comparison then can be used to establish a relationship between energy of position and energy of motion.

MATERIALS (per team)
    2 sections of grooved track
    Tape
    2 marbles
    2 steel balls
    Timer
    Block of wood
    Strip of paper
    3 x 5 index card

PROCEDURES

A. Place the two sections of grooved track together as shown in Figure 9 · 3, and fasten them with tape. Raise one end of the track and place the block under it—about 5 cm from the raised end. Be sure a steel ball or marble can roll smoothly from one section of the track to the other.

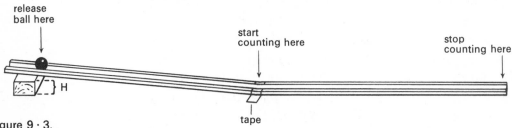

Figure 9 · 3.
Set-up for Procedures A and B.

B. Put a steel ball on the track directly above the point supported by the block. Turn the timer on and release the ball. Start counting when the ball reaches the level section of track. Stop counting when it reaches the end of the level track. Measure and record the length of the level track. Record the time required for the ball to travel that distance.

C. Move the support block so that it is under the *middle* of the inclined track. Again place a steel ball on the track just above the point supported by the block. Release the ball, and measure the time required for the ball to roll the length of the level track. Even though the incline is steeper, note that the ball will experience the same change in height as it did in Procedure B. Record the time required for the ball to travel the length of the level track.

Figure 9 · 4.
Set-up for
Procedure C.

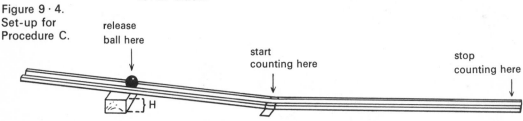

INTERPRETATIONS

1. Calculate the speed of the ball on the level track in Procedures B and C. Move the support block to a point halfway between the midpoint of the inclined track and its lower end, as shown in Figure 9 · 5. Predict the amount of time the ball will take to travel the length of the level track. Record your prediction.

Figure 9 · 5. Set-up for Interpretation 1.

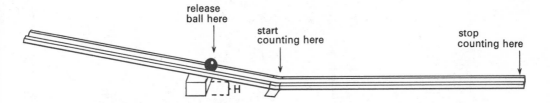

release ball here

start counting here

stop counting here

H

PROCEDURES (continued)

D. Test the prediction you made in Interpretation 1.

INTERPRETATIONS (continued)

2. What effect did changing the slope in Procedures C and D have on the speed of the ball on the level track?

3. In these trials, what was the relationship between the *height* from which the ball was released on the inclined track and the *speed* of the ball on the level track?

PROCEDURES (continued)

E. Return the support block to the midpoint of the inclined track. Fasten the strip of paper to the side of the inclined track. Hold a 3 x 5 card on edge next to the level track as shown in Figure 9 · 6. Place a mark on the card at the level of the track. Label this mark *0*.

Figure 9 · 6. Set-up for Procedure E.

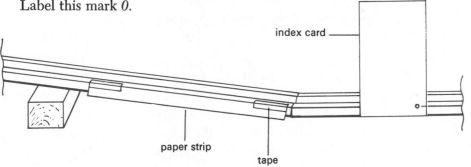

index card

paper strip

tape

Measuring up from zero, mark off and label the following distances on the card: 1 cm, 2 cm, 3 cm, 4 cm (Figure 9 · 7).

Figure 9 · 7.
Carrying out
Procedure E.

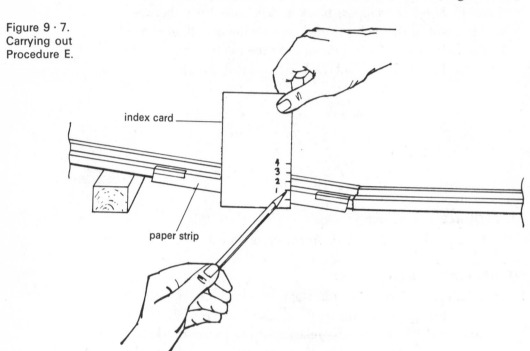

index card

paper strip

Hold the card on the table in an upright position again, and slide it along the inclined section of the track until the 1-cm mark on the card is just even with the top edge of the track. Be sure to hold the card straight so that the measurements of vertical distance are correct. Hold a sharp pencil against the edge of the card at this point, and draw a vertical line on the paper strip attached to the inclined track. A ball released at this point on the track will fall 1 cm before it starts rolling on the level track. Use the index card to mark release points on the inclined track that are 2, 3, and 4 cm above the level track.

F. Place the ball at the 4-cm mark, and release it. Record the time required for the ball to roll the length of the level track. Repeat several times, and record the average of the trials.

G. Repeat Procedure F for each of the heights marked.

INTERPRETATIONS (continued)

4. Calculate the average speed of the ball on the level track for each of the release points. Prepare a graph as shown in Figure 9 · 8. Plot the average speed for each release point.

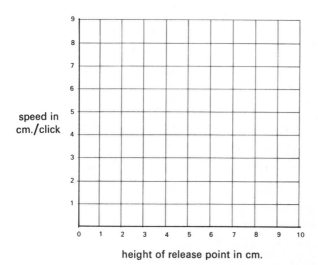

speed in cm./click

height of release point in cm.

Figure 9 · 8.

5. If you double the height of the release point, does the ball roll twice as fast?

6. Calculate the values for the following ratios:

a. $\dfrac{\text{speed from 2-cm height}}{\text{speed from 1-cm height}} =$

b. $\dfrac{\text{speed from 4-cm height}}{\text{speed from 2-cm height}} =$

c. $\dfrac{\text{speed from 4-cm height}}{\text{speed from 1-cm height}} =$

7. Suppose you want the ball to roll twice as fast on the level track as it did when you released it from the 2-cm mark. From what height should you release it?

PROCEDURES (continued)

H. Place a marble at the 4-cm mark on the inclined track. Release the marble. Measure and record the time required for the marble to roll the length of the level track.

INTERPRETATIONS (continued)

8. Calculate the speed of the marble on the level track.
9. Compare the speed gained by a marble in Procedure H with the speed gained by a steel ball in Procedure F.

PROCEDURES (continued)

I. Place a marble on the track where the two sections are joined. Place a steel ball at the 4-cm mark on the inclined track. Release the steel ball. Measure and record the time required for the *steel ball* to roll the length of the level track.

J. Repeat Procedure I, but replace the steel ball with a second marble. Measure and record the time required for *the marble you released* to roll the length of the level track. (It will be rolling behind the first marble.)

INTERPRETATIONS (continued)

10. Why was the measured time in Procedure I different from the measured time in Procedure J?

Note: Procedures K through N and Interpretations 11 through 14 are optional.

PROCEDURES (continued)

K. Use a balance to measure the mass of the steel ball and the mass of the marble. Record these masses.

INTERPRETATIONS (continued)

11. Calculate the momentum of the marble rolling on the level track after it has been released from a height of 4 cm.
12. a. For the steel ball to have a momentum equal to the momentum you calculated for the marble, what must be the speed of the steel ball?
    b. Calculate the time required for the steel ball to roll the

length of the level track if it has the speed determined in
Interpretation 12a.

c. Use the graph you prepared in Interpretation 4 to determine the height from which the steel ball should be released if it is to have the speed calculated in Interpretation
12a.

PROCEDURES (continued)

L. Place the steel ball on the inclined track at the height you
calculated in Interpretation 12c. Release the ball and determine the time required for it to roll the length of the level
track. If the time required to roll the length of the level track
is not the same as the time you calculated in Interpretation
12b, move the ball to a different position. Continue the trials
until the calculated time and the observed time are the same.
Record the height of the ball in the final position.

INTERPRETATIONS (continued)

13. Suppose that a rolling steel ball collides with a stationary
steel ball. If a marble (rolling with the same momentum)
collides with a stationary steel ball, would the rolling ball and
the rolling marble behave in the same way? Record your
prediction.

PROCEDURES (continued)

M. Place a steel ball on the track where the two sections join.
Place the other steel ball at the position on the inclined track
determined in Procedure L. Release the ball and record the
result of the collision.

N. Place a steel ball on the track where the two sections join.
Place a marble on the inclined track at the 4-cm mark. Release
the marble and record the result of the collision.

INTERPRETATIONS (continued)

14. Since both the steel ball and the marble had the same momentum, how can you account for the results observed in
Procedures M and N?

You have seen that energy of position (or gravitational energy) can be converted into energy of motion. Objects that fall through a particular distance always gain the same amount of speed, no matter how heavy they are.

Doubling the distance of fall does not double the speed. Doubling the distance of fall *does* double the energy of motion. Experiments have shown that the energy of motion of an object increases in direct proportion to the square of the speed. You have seen that the energy of motion is greater for a heavy object than for a light object, if both have the same momentum.

Energy of motion is determined by multiplying the mass of an object by the square of its speed, or mv^2. In Section Eleven you will study the relationship between energy of motion and heat energy. Both of these concepts must be included in a model that is useful in explaining the behavior of matter.

Energy Conversion

It takes energy to lift a ball to the top of an inclined plane. The higher the ball is lifted, the greater the amount of energy required. In Investigation 28 you found that the *force* required to lift a ball is the same no matter how high it is lifted. Energy depends upon two factors: (1) *force*, and (2) *distance through which that force is exerted*.

After a ball is lifted to the top of a track, it possesses energy of position, which can be converted into other kinds of energy. The energy possessed by a motionless ball at the top of the track is called *potential energy*, which (in this case) is the result of the force of gravity. Gravitational force causes the ball to accelerate as it rolls to a lower level. A rolling ball possesses energy because it is in motion. The potential energy is gradually changed to energy of motion as the ball moves downhill.

Suppose you add a second inclined plane at the other end of the level track (Figure 9 · 9). When the ball begins rolling uphill, its energy of motion will again be converted to potential energy, and it will slow down. If we ignore friction, we might expect the ball to roll up the second inclined plane until it reaches a height equal to that of its starting point.

Figure 9 · 9.

A   A′

center   center

Working with a pendulum, we can see a similar example of the change from potential energy to energy of motion and back to potential energy. When a pendulum completes a swing, it comes to a brief but complete stop. At that moment, it has no energy of motion—only potential energy. At the center of its swing, on the other hand, it has no available potential energy—only energy of motion (Figure 9 · 10).

Figure 9 · 10.
The positions of
highest potential
energy and no
energy of motion
are *A* and *A'*. *C*
is the position of
lowest potential
energy and high-
est energy of
motion. If the
pendulum swings
from A to *A'*, *B*
represents the
range of *decreas-
ing* potential
energy and
increasing energy
of motion. *D*
represents the
range of *increas-
ing* potential
energy and
decreasing
energy of motion.

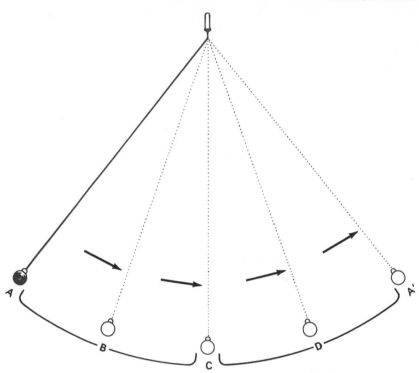

Energy of motion carries the swinging pendulum to its highest point at the end of the swing. Except at the highest and lowest points, both potential energy and energy of motion are present in constantly changing proportions.

INVESTIGATION 33: A Study of the Pendulum

The pendulum was one of the first devices used to study time, the force of gravity, and other aspects of physical science. A pendulum is a relatively easy piece of equipment to build, but its behavior is not always easy to explain.

MATERIALS (per team)
   2 lead sinkers of different weights
   White thread and marking pen
   Screw fastener or other means of attaching the pendulum
   Watch with sweep second hand
   Meterstick

PROCEDURES

A. Attach one end of the thread to a fixed support. Tie the heaviest sinker to the other end (Figure 9 · 11). Pull the pendulum

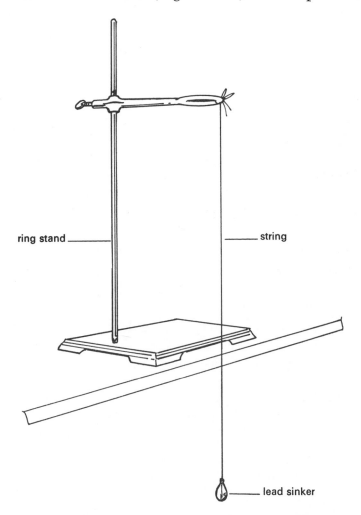

Figure 9 · 11.
Set-up for
Procedures A–C.

ring stand

string

lead sinker

weight about 20 cm from its rest position. Release, and determine how many complete swings (round trips) the weight will make in one minute. Repeat, starting at three or four other distances—such as 15 cm, 10 cm, 5 cm, and so forth—from rest position. For each distance determine the number of complete swings of the pendulum weight per minute. Record your data on a table similar to Figure 9 · 12. (The time required for one complete round trip is called the *period* of the pendulum.)

Figure 9 · 12.

Trial	Distance From Rest Position	Complete Swings Per Minute	Period (seconds per swing)
1	20 cm		
2			
3			
4			

INTERPRETATIONS

1. According to your data, what is the period of your pendulum?
2. What seems to be the relationship between the distance a pendulum swings and its period?
3. What would be the period of your pendulum if you released it at a distance of 50 cm from its rest position?

PROCEDURES (continued)

B. Repeat Procedure A, but use a lighter sinker. Be sure that the length of the thread is the same as in Procedure A. Before beginning, predict what effect a lighter weight will have on the number of swings per minute. Record your data on a chart like the one used in Procedure A.

INTERPRETATIONS (continued)

4. Was your prediction correct?
5. What do you think is the relationship between a pendulum's weight and its period?

PROCEDURES (continued)

C. Using the heaviest sinker again, and using the same length of thread, cause the pendulum to swing in a circle instead of a straight path. First predict and then determine the number of times per minute the weight completes a circular path. Try other variations of this experiment. Use sinkers of different weights. Cause the sinker to move in an oval path instead of a circular one.

INTERPRETATIONS (continued)

6. What is the relationship of the path of a pendulum to its period?
7. How do the weight, distance, and path of a pendulum affect its period?
8. In your use of a pendulum so far, the weight, distance traveled, and path of swing have varied. The length of the thread remained constant (fixed). Will the pendulum's period be affected if you keep the weight and distance constant but vary the length of the thread? Write a prediction in your notebook.

PROCEDURES (continued)

D. Obtain a thread about 2.5 meters long and attach it to the heavy sinker. Lay the thread and weight along a meterstick. Stretch the thread, and mark it at the following distances from the center of the weight: 25, 50, 75, 100, 150, and 200 cm.
E. Choose a distance to swing the pendulum (from 5 to 10 cm). Mark this distance in some way so that the pendulum will start at the same release point in all of your trials. You might mark the distance by standing a book or a ring stand at the desired distance from the rest position of the pendulum.
F. Copy Figure 9 · 13. Determine the period of the pendulum for each of the six thread lengths. Record your data.

Figure 9 · 13.

Length	Distance From Rest Position	Number of Complete Swings per Minute	Period
200 cm			
150 cm			
100 cm			
75 cm			
50 cm			
25 cm			

INTERPRETATIONS (continued)

9. How did changing the length of the pendulum affect the period?

10. Make a graph of your data. From your graph, find the period for each of the following lengths.

Figure 9 · 14.

Length in cm	20	30	40	50	60	80	100	160	200
Period in Seconds									

11. One useful way to analyze data is to compare ratios. Predict how doubling the length of the pendulum would affect its period. For each ratio shown below, substitute the values obtained in Interpretation 10, and divide the denominator into the numerator. Compare the values obtained.

$$\frac{\text{period for 40 cm}}{\text{period for 20 cm}} =$$

$$\frac{\text{period for 80 cm}}{\text{period for 40 cm}} =$$

$$\frac{\text{period for 120 cm}}{\text{period for 60 cm}} =$$

$$\frac{\text{period for 200 cm}}{\text{period for 100 cm}} =$$

$$\frac{\text{period for 60 cm}}{\text{period for 30 cm}} =$$

$$\frac{\text{period for 100 cm}}{\text{period for 50 cm}} =$$

$$\frac{\text{period for 160 cm}}{\text{period for 80 cm}} =$$

12. What determines the period of a pendulum?

13. As an additional activity at home, you might construct a much longer pendulum and test Interpretations 10 and 11.

REFERENCES

Andrade, Edward. *Sir Isaac Newton: His Life and Work.* ("Science Study Series") Garden City, N.Y.: Doubleday & Co. (Anchor Books), Inc., 1958.

Bixby, William G. *Universe of Galileo and Newton.* New York: Harper and Row, 1964.

Blackwood, Paul E. *Push and Pull: The Story of Energy.* New York: McGraw-Hill Book Co., 1959.

Lehrman, R.L., and Scwartz, C. *Foundations of Physics.* New York: Holt, Rinehart & Winston, Inc., 1965.

O'Brien, Robert. *Machines.* New York: Time Inc. (Time-Life Books), 1965.

PSSC. *Physics.* Boston: D. C. Heath & Co., 1965.

Ruchlis, Hyman. *Orbit: A Picture of Force and Motion.* New York: Harper and Row, 1958.

Sootin, Harry. *Isaac Newton.* New York: Simon & Schuster (Julian Messner, Inc.), 1955.

Phases of Matter

Most science textbooks classify matter into three forms, or phases: solids, liquids, and gases. But why is a solid *solid*, a liquid *liquid*, and a gas *gas*? Are each of these phases the result of chemical interactions, or of a combination of both chemical and physical interactions? Are there really only three phases of matter? The next series of investigations should help you to resolve some of these questions.

INVESTIGATION 34: Calibrating a Thermometer

A thermometer is useful for measuring changes in temperature. Thermometers can also reveal information about relationships between matter and energy. Like most scientific instruments, thermometers vary in cost from a few pennies to hundreds of dollars. Selection of a thermometer depends upon the purpose for which it is to be used. Because you will not need to make exact measurements of variations in temperature, an inexpensive thermometer will be used in this investigation.

There are many kinds of thermometers. You will use an alcohol thermometer. The thermometers doctors use to measure body heat contain mercury instead of alcohol. When the temperature of liquids such as alcohol or mercury is increased, their volumes increase. When a given amount of such a liquid is confined within a tube, an increase in volume results in a longer column of liquid. Therefore the longer a column of alcohol or mercury, the higher the temperature. Lower temperatures are indicated by a decrease in length of the liquid column.

Our first task will be to calibrate (mark) temperature on an alcohol thermometer. We will then use this thermometer to investigate certain properties of matter that involve both chemical and physical interactions.

MATERIALS (per student)
 Uncalibrated alcohol thermometer
 2 glass microscope slides
 Plastic millimeter rule

MATERIALS (per team)
 Roll of freezer tape
 Water bath
 Beaker of crushed ice
 Piece of cardboard to cover beaker
 Scissors

PROCEDURES

At sea level water boils at 100°C (212°F) and freezes at 0°C (32°F). The boiling point decreases about 1°C for each 1000-foot increase in elevation. We can use the boiling and freezing points of water to locate temperature values on our thermometer.

A. Cut a piece of freezer tape about 6 mm wide and equal to the length of your thermometer (with the bulb exposed). Place this tape on the glass microscope slides as illustrated in Figure 10 · 1.

B. Prepare a water bath as shown in Figure 10 · 2. Place the thermometer in the beaker of water. The level of alcohol will continue to rise until the water boils. When the water boils, the alcohol should stop rising and remain at a fixed level. Measure

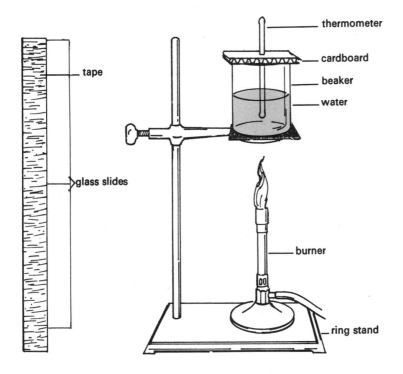

thermometer

cardboard

beaker

water

tape

glass slides

burner

ring stand

Fig. 10 · 1. (Left)
Set-up for
Procedure A.

Fig. 10 · 2. (Rt.)
Set-up for
Procedure B.

the distance (in mm) from the *top* of the thermometer to the top of the alcohol. Record this measurement in your notebook.

C. Allow the thermometer to cool. Then immerse it for several minutes in a beaker or jar half-filled with crushed ice (see Figure 10 · 3). When the length of the alcohol column no

Herb Comess

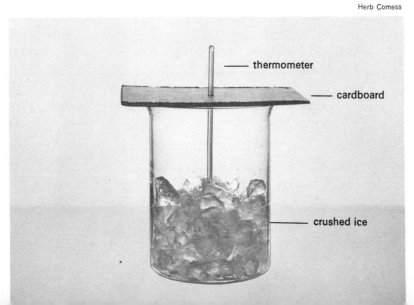

thermometer

cardboard

crushed ice

Figure 10 · 3.
Set-up for
Procedure C.

longer changes, measure the distance from the top of the thermometer to the top of the alcohol. Record this measurement in your notebook.

D. Use an atlas to find the elevation (height above sea level) in your area. Assuming that the boiling point decreases 1°C per 1000 feet above sea level, calculate the boiling point of water in your area.

E. Measuring from the top of the tape, mark off a distance equal to the distance you recorded when the thermometer was in boiling water. Label this point *100°C* or whatever the boiling point of water is in your area (see Procedure D). Again measuring from the top of the tape, mark off a distance equal to the distance you recorded when the thermometer was immersed in the beaker of ice. Make another mark on the tape at this point, and label it *0°C*.

F. Place your ruler alongside the tape so that 0 mm is aligned with 0°C. Calculate the number of mm to the point midway between 0°C and the boiling point. Mark this point and label it *50°C* (or less, if you live in an area that is 1000 feet or more above sea level). For example, suppose the distance from 0° to 100° on your tape is 60 mm. Half of 60 is 30, so you would place a mark at 30 mm. If the elevation of your area is only a little above sea level, you would label it *50°C*. But if you

Figure 10 · 4. Calibrating tape for a thermometer.

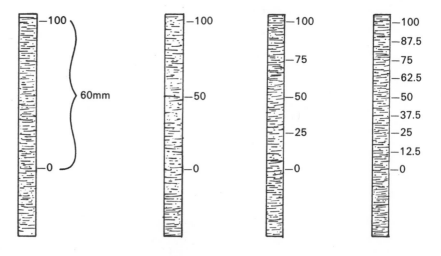

found that your area is about 5000 feet above sea level, the boiling point of water would be approximately 95°C. Therefore the mark halfway between 95° and 0° would be 47.5°C. Mark off and label as many intermediate units as possible on your tape (see Figure 10 · 4).

You might calibrate your thermometer by determining degrees per millimeter. If 100°C is equivalent to 60 mm, then 10°C is equivalent to 6 mm. You could then mark your tape at 6-mm intervals to indicate each 10-degree difference in temperature.

G. In your notebook make an exact copy, *to scale*, of the marks on your tape. Carefully remove the tape from the glass slides. Fasten it to the thermometer so that the top end of the tape is exactly even with the top end of the thermometer. The tape should not mask the alcohol in the tube. The bulb at the bottom must not be covered with tape.

H. Test your thermometer. Determine room temperature, your own body temperature, and the temperature of tap water.

CAUTION: *Do not place an unsterilized thermometer in your mouth. To measure body temperature, place it under your arm or hold it in the palm of your hand.*

I. If possible, compare your results with results obtained with mercury thermometers. How does the accuracy of your thermometer compare with those used for professional purposes?

J. Place the thermometer in a safe place until needed.

PROBLEMS

1. In a thermometer, a change in the height of a column of liquid indicates a change in temperature. Using your understanding of the nature of matter, explain why the height of the column of liquid in a thermometer increases with the temperature.

2. The most accurate thermometers are not of the liquid-glass type. From your experience in calibrating a thermometer, and from a comparison of your thermometer with those of other students in your class, suggest possible reasons for this.

Structure of Water Molecules

All life on earth depends upon water in one way or another. Until recent times, when people talked about "natural resources," they mentioned oil, iron ore, forests, and so forth, but seldom included water. Yet water is probably our most important natural resource.

Early alchemists searched for a universal solvent, a liquid in which anything would dissolve. Such a solvent has never been discovered and probably does not exist. Water comes closest to this ideal; more kinds of substances will dissolve in water than in any other known liquid. Much of our knowledge of chemistry is based on the relationship between molecules of water and molecules of other substances.

So far we have used the formula H_2O to indicate water. This formula tells us that there are 2 hydrogen atoms and 1 oxygen atom in a water molecule, but it does not tell us how the atoms are arranged in the molecule. Chemists use a different kind of formula to show the arrangement of atoms in a molecule. Remember that formulas are only models and not pictures of actual atoms.

For convenience we may wish to represent a water molecule in this way:

$$H\text{-}O\text{-}H$$

Then we could write the equation for a reaction between sodium (Na) and water thus:

$$2 \text{ Na} + 2\text{H-O-H} \longrightarrow 2\text{Na-O-H} + \text{H-H}$$

The dashes represent *electron bonds* that hold the atoms together. Many reactions are written this way, because it is a convenient method of conveying information, as we will see later.

Recall that angles are measured in degrees. A circle has 360 degrees; half a circle, 180 degrees; a quarter of a circle (a right angle), 90 degrees; and so forth. This same system is used to measure the angles formed by chemical bonds. Chemists' experiments indicate that this kind of model of a water molecule should be written H-O-H instead of H-O-H, because the three atoms apparently are not arranged in a straight line. Experiments also indicate that the angle formed by bonds between the three atoms is about 105° (Figure 10 • 5).

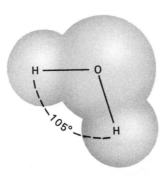

Figure 10 · 5. Structural model of a water molecule, with an angle of 105° between the bonds.

The angle between the bonds in a molecule is important because it is related to the concept of *polarity*. A molecule is said to be polar when one side of it is more negatively charged than another. Recall that electrons carry a negative charge. In a polar molecule electrons tend to move toward one side, giving the molecule positive and negative regions.

With sensitive apparatus, the polarity of water molecules can be demonstrated by placing a container of water between two electrically charged plates. Many of the water molecules line up so that the positive poles of the molecules face the negative plate, and the negative poles of the molecules face the positive plate (see Figure 10 · 6).

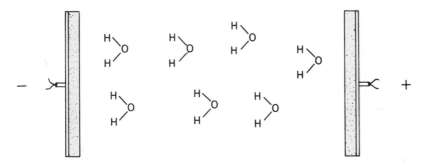

Figure 10 · 6. Diagram showing orientation of water molecules in an electric field.

The polarity of a molecule is determined by two factors: (1) the kinds of atoms that make up the molecule, and (2) the angles formed by the bonds. In a water molecule, the hydrogen atoms attract electrons less strongly than the oxygen atom does. This causes the hydrogen atoms to have a positive charge and the oxygen atom to have a negative charge.

If the three atoms in a water molecule were arranged in a straight line (Figure 10 · 7A), each end would be positive, and the center would be negative. Such a molecule would not be polar because it would not have a negative end.

However, the actual bond angle of water molecules has been established as about 105° (Figure 10 · 7B). The oxygen atom, which has a negative charge, lies to one side rather than just between the two hydrogen atoms, which have positive charges. Therefore, the water molecule is polar.

Figure 10 · 7. Diagram showing two possible arrangements of atoms in a water molecule. The arrangement in A would cause zero polarity. Only the arrangement in B agrees with the actual data.

The carbon dioxide (CO_2) molecule does not appear to be polar; it is thought to have a structure like that in Figure 10 · 8.

Figure 10 · 8. Diagram of a carbon dioxide molecule with zero polarity.

The angles formed by bonds are not the only factors that determine polarity. The atoms of some elements attract electrons better than others. A hydrogen chloride (HCl) molecule is electrically neutral, yet it is polar because Cl attracts electrons more strongly than H. Thus H-Cl molecules would line up in an electrical field with their hydrogen (positive) ends toward the negative pole and their chloride (negative) ends toward the positive pole. A hydrogen molecule (H-H) is nonpolar, since the attraction of electrons is no stronger in one atom than in the other.

Understanding the behavior of polar and nonpolar molecules is important, because it will help you interpret the results of many investigations to follow.

PROBLEMS

1. Atoms that tend to gain electrons form negative ions. Atoms that tend to lose electrons form positive ions. Which family on your modified periodic chart (page 78) has atoms that are most likely to form the negative part of a polar molecule? Which family has atoms that are most likely to form the positive part of a polar molecule?

2. If the angle between the bonds of a water molecule were 90°, would you expect the polarity of this molecule to be greater or less than that of a normal water molecule? Explain your answer.

INVESTIGATION 35: Water and Ice

Like many liquids, water contracts as it cools—its volume decreases. When the temperature reaches about 4°C, however, water starts to behave in a different way. In this investigation you will observe the volume of a sample of water in two phases, solid and liquid.

MATERIALS (per team)
   Test tube containing ice
   Metric ruler

PROCEDURES

A. Measure and record the depth of the ice in the tube.
B. Melt the ice by holding the test tube in your hand. Be careful not to spill any water.
C. Measure and record the depth of water in the tube.

INTERPRETATIONS

1. Suggest a model that might explain the change in volume as ice melts to form water. Your model should take into account the shape and polarity of water molecules, and the difference between particles in a liquid and in a solid.
2. According to your model, which should have a greater density —ice or water?

INVESTIGATION 36: Ice, Salt, Sugar, and Alcohol

At sea level water boils at 100°C and freezes at 0°C. Body temperature, room temperature, and the temperature of tap water all fall somewhere between 0°C and 100°C. In this investigation you will study temperatures that are below 0°C.

MATERIALS (per student)
    250-ml beaker, jar, or drinking glass
    Alcohol thermometer (used in Investigation 34)
    Spoon or mixing stick

MATERIALS (per class)
    Finely crushed ice
    Table salt
    Table sugar
    Ditto fluid or wood (methyl) alcohol

PROCEDURES
A. Calibrate your alcohol thermometer below the zero mark. Do this by assuming that the liquid in your thermometer will move the same distance per degree below zero as it does per degree above zero. Mark the tape (in degrees centigrade) as accurately as possible.
B. Pour crushed ice into the 250-ml beaker or jar until it is about half-full.
C. Insert your thermometer into the crushed ice so that the bulb is well below the surface.
D. When the reading is 0°C, add an amount of table salt equal to about one-third the amount of ice. Mix well with a small spoon or stick, while holding the thermometer in position. Carefully observe the thermometer for five minutes. Record the new temperature. Empty and rinse the beaker.
E. Repeat Procedures A, B, and C, but use sugar in place of salt. Record your observations. Repeat again, using alcohol instead of salt or sugar. Record your observations.

INTERPRETATIONS

1. How does salt cause the change in temperature you observed? In answering this question, consider the structure of a water molecule and the electrical conductivity of salt in solution.
2. Why is salt sprinkled on roads during the winter in some parts of the country?
3. Explain why salt, sugar, and alcohol each cause a different temperature change when added to crushed ice.

OPTIONAL PROBLEM

The molecular weights of methyl alcohol, table sugar (sucrose), and common salt (NaCl) are 32, 342, and 58.5, respectively. Each "molecule" of NaCl forms one sodium ion and one chloride ion. These ions behave as free particles in solution. Each molecule of sugar or of alcohol exists as a single particle in solution.

Suppose you prepared the solutions listed in Figure 10 · 9. Then suppose you measured the freezing point of each solution with a very accurate thermometer and obtained the data shown in the table. (Recall that the freezing point of pure water is 0°C.)

Figure 10 · 9.

Grams of table sugar per liter of solution	10	20	40	80
Freezing point	−0.06°C	−0.11°C	−0.22°C	−0.44°C
Grams of methyl alcohol per liter of solution	10	20	40	80
Freezing point	−0.57°C	−1.14°C	−2.30°C	−4.60°C
Grams of sodium chloride per liter of solution	10	20	40	80
Freezing point	−0.60°C	−1.17°C	−2.32°C	−4.63°C

1. For each solution, calculate the number of moles in 80 grams.
2. For one mole of particles, how much would the temperature be lowered?

INVESTIGATION 37: Behavior of Matter Under Condition of Low Temperature (Optional)

Many gases such as nitrogen, oxygen, and hydrogen, can be liquefied. In a liquid state these gases are extremely cold. A rubber ball, a piece of celery, a hot dog, or a person's finger, if immersed in these liquids, freezes almost instantly and becomes extremely brittle.

This investigation will deal with the behavior of matter under conditions of extreme cold.

MATERIALS (per student)
   Calibrated alcohol thermometer
   Dry ice
   Sack (heavy cloth or heavy paper)
   250-ml Pyrex beaker
   Ice water
   Pyrex test tube
   Ditto fluid

CAUTION: *Dry ice is extremely cold and may cause severe injury if it is allowed to come in contact with your hands. Use tongs, pliers, or asbestos gloves to handle dry ice.*

PROCEDURES
A. Place dry ice in a heavy cloth or paper sack and crush with a hammer until the dry ice has the consistency of coarse sand.
B. Pour crushed dry ice into a 250-ml Pyrex beaker until it is half-full.
C. Pre-cool your calibrated alcohol thermometer in ice water. Insert the thermometer into the dry ice, and determine the temperature as accurately as possible. Record in your notebook.

D. Half-fill a Pyrex test tube with ditto fluid, and mark the level carefully. Then carefully lower the tube into the dry ice. Wait five minutes and then remove the tube. Was there any change in the volume of the ditto fluid? Try to obtain the same results by leaving a test tube of ditto fluid in a freezing compartment overnight.

INTERPRETATIONS

1. Compare ditto fluid with water in terms of
   a. change in volume from liquid to solid
   b. freezing point.
2. Why is there such a difference between the temperature of dry ice and that of ordinary ice?

The Nature of Heat: A Problem

We have now worked with temperatures ranging from about 100°C to far below 0°C. When water reaches a certain temperature it boils, and if this temperature is maintained the water will soon "disappear." When water is kept between 100°C and 0°C it will remain in a liquid phase, with only very slow evaporation taking place. The higher the temperature, the greater the rate of evaporation. If we lower the temperature of water to 0°C, it begins to freeze. As you have seen, ice has properties quite unlike those of water. If ice is left outdoors even in sub-zero temperature, it too may slowly change to vapor. After examining Figure 10 · 10, think of a model to explain the different stages in the evaporation of water.

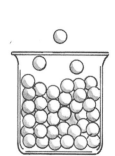 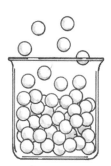 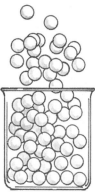

Figure 10 · 10. Diagramatic drawing of the different stages in the evaporation of water.

Your problem is to explain heat in terms of the experiments you have performed. What relationship exists between heat and the behavior of water molecules? Base your explanations on the behavior of molecules, the behavior of demons, or some other theory. Be prepared to defend your argument. Prepare a model as part of your explanation of heat. How useful your model will be depends on how well you have studied previous parts of this course and upon how ingenious you are in putting your knowledge to work.

REFERENCES

Adler, Irving. *Hot and Cold.* New York: John Day Co., Inc., 1959.

Davis, Kenneth S., and Day, John A. *Water: The Mirror of Science.* ("Science Study Series") Garden City, N.Y.: Doubleday & Co., Inc. (Anchor Books), 1961.

Roller, Duane E. *Early Development of the Concepts of Temperature and Heat.* Cambridge, Mass.: Harvard University Press, 1950.

Weisskopf, Victor F. *Knowledge and Wonder: The Natural World as Man Knows It.* ("Science Study Series") Garden City, N.Y.: Doubleday & Co., Inc. (Anchor Books), 1963.

Heat Energy

Early Greek writers believed that heat is a substance and that it moves from a hot object into a cold object. This model of heat was used by most scientists for many centuries. During the 1700's several scientists developed the concept that heat is a fluid that flows freely from one object to another. This fluid was named *caloric*. It was thought that an atom of any substance is surrounded by caloric fluid. According to this model, if an object is heated, the spaces between its atoms will be filled with more caloric. An object with lots of space between its atoms will hold more caloric than an object that has small spaces between its atoms. The caloric model was a success because it explained all observations of heat made in its time.

The development of reliable thermometers during the eighteenth century made it possible to conduct experiments involving precise temperature measurements. In 1714, the German physicist Gabriel Fahrenheit made a mercury thermometer and developed the Fahrenheit temperature scale. On the Fahrenheit scale 32° is the freezing point of water and 212° is the boiling point of water. In 1742, the Swedish astronomer and physicist Anders Celcius devised a temperature scale on which 0° is the freezing point of water and 100° is the boiling point. This became known as the *centigrade* scale—from the Latin words meaning hundred steps.[1] The two scales are compared in Appendix C at the back of the book.

Benjamin Thompson, later known as Count Rumford (1753–1814), was interested in the nature of heat. Rumford owned one of the most precise balances available in the eighteenth century. He weighed water and other substances before and after heating or cooling them. In his experiments he could find no evidence that any fluid enters an object during heating or leaves it during cooling. For example, he noticed that a cannon became very hot while the barrel was being bored. He could find nothing to indicate that the boring added anything to the metal. Instead he suggested that heat results from the motion of particles. As matter is heated, the speed of these particles increases; as matter is cooled, these particles slow down. According to this theory, heat is a form of energy. Today we call this theory the *kinetic* theory of heat.

In the next series of investigations you will examine various characteristics of heat. As you complete them, you should attempt to explain results in terms of the kinetic theory of heat. At the end of each investigation, be prepared to explain the effects of heat in terms of the motion of molecules.

INVESTIGATION 38: Energy Transfer

Your present understanding of force and energy may be different from what it was when you started this course. You should have learned the difference between kinetic energy and potential energy and how one can be converted to the other.

There are many ways in which potential energy can be converted to kinetic energy. The most familiar source of energy to you, though you may not have thought of it this way, is the food you eat. In this investigation *you* will provide the source of poten-

---

[1]By an agreement at an international conference of scientists in 1948, it was decided that the centigrade scale be changed to the *Celsius* scale. Because most people are still more familiar with the term *centigrade,* we will use it throughout the book.

tial energy. Your muscles will convert some of the potential chemical energy in the food you have eaten into kinetic energy—energy of motion. You will observe the effect of transferring this energy to a sample of water.

MATERIALS (per team)
    Graduated cylinder
    2 glass jars with screw lids
    Thermometer
    Newspaper
    Tape

PROCEDURES

A. Pour 20 ml of water into each of the two glass jars. Record the water temperatures. If you use one of the alcohol thermometers calibrated in Section Ten, mark the initial level of the alcohol with a piece of tape on the stem of the thermometer.

B. Tighten the lids on the jars. Wrap both jars in newspaper, as shown in Figure 11 · 1. When you are finished the jars will be wrapped in at least eight thicknesses of paper. The paper will act as a heat insulator.

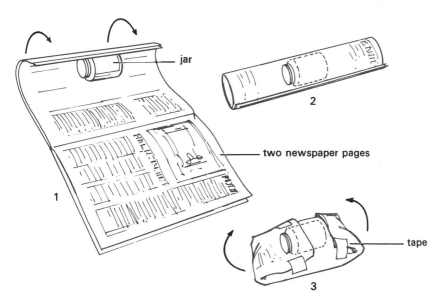

jar

two newspaper pages

tape

Figure 11 · 1.
Carrying out
Procedure B.

C. Shake one jar vigorously (about four times per second) for four minutes. Members of the team may take turns doing this so that the shaking continues at a rapid pace. In shaking the jar, move it less than two inches, back and forth. Do not shake the second jar.

D. Unwrap the jars. Remove the lids and again record the temperature of the water in each.

INTERPRETATIONS

1. Calculate the temperature change (if any) in each jar, and record in your notebook. You have learned how units for measuring length, volume, and mass developed. You have used other units to measure temperature (usually degrees centigrade or degrees Fahrenheit). The unit for measuring heat energy is the *calorie*. One calorie is the amount of heat energy required to raise the temperature of 1 gram of water 1°C. How many grams of water did you place in each jar? How many calories were gained by the water in each jar?

2. Using the kinetic theory of heat, explain any temperature changes you observed.

    Scientists often measure heat in *kilocalories* when dealing with larger amounts of heat. The kilocalorie is the amount of heat energy required to raise the temperature of 1 kilogram of water 1°C. Thus the kilocalorie is equal to 1000 calories. The kilocalorie is often abbreviated as *Calorie* or *Cal.*, with a capital C. The familiar calories used in measuring the energy content of foods are kilocalories.

PROBLEMS

1. How many calories will be needed to raise the temperature of 50 grams of water from 5°C to 85°C?

2. One kilogram of water cooled from its boiling temperature (at sea level) to freezing. How many calories were lost by the water?

We have defined a calorie as the amount of energy required to raise the temperature of 1 gram of water 1°C. Water can store heat energy. Other liquids, as well as metals, can also store heat energy. But different materials have different capacities for heat storage. The heat-storing capacity of equal weights of water and a metal will be compared during this investigation. Before performing the investigation, predict which has the greater heat-storing capacity—a metal or water.

MATERIALS (per team)

> 2 Styrofoam cups
> Graduated cylinder
> Balance sensitive to 1 gram
> Thread
> Metal weight
> Pyrex beaker
> Burner
> Thermometer

PROCEDURES

A. Label the Styrofoam cups *A* and *B*. Pour 40 ml of tap water into each cup.

B. Using the balance, determine the weight of the metal to the nearest gram. Tie a 10-inch length of thread to the metal. Weigh out an amount of tap water equal to the weight of the metal.

C. Place the metal object and water from Procedure B in a beaker, and heat to about 80°C. (Allow the thread attached to the metal to hang over the edge of the beaker.)

D. When the temperature of the water has reached 80°C, transfer the metal to Cup *A* and pour the hot water into Cup *B*. Stir the contents of both cups for one minute. Then record the water temperature in each cup.

INTERPRETATIONS

1. Which contains more heat energy—metal at 80°C, or an equal weight of water at 80°C?

2. Using the kinetic theory of heat and what you have learned about the structure and behavior of matter, explain your answer to Interpretation 1.

INVESTIGATION 40: Heat and Temperature

MATERIALS (per team)

    About 40 grams of ice

    100-ml graduated cylinder (heat-resistant plastic or Pyrex)

    3 Styrofoam cups

    Balance sensitive to at least 0.1 gram

    250-ml Pyrex beaker

    Ring stand, ring, and wire gauze

    Burner

    Ice

    2 thermometers

    Small spoon or mixing stick

PROCEDURES

A. Label the Styrofoam cups *A*, *B*, and *C*. Mix about 40 grams of ice and 40 grams of cold water together in Cup C.

B. Weigh Cups A and B. Record the weights in your notebook.

C. Pour 200 ml of tap water into a beaker, and heat to boiling. While the water is heating, complete Procedures D, E, and F. When the water starts to boil, turn off the heat and set the beaker of hot water aside for use in Procedures G and H.

D. Pour 40 grams of water from the ice-and-water mixture into Cup A.

E. Place Cup B on the balance, and add about 20 grams of ice. The amount added should be weighed as accurately as possible. Record the weight of the ice in your notebook. Pour water from the ice-and-water mixture into Cup B until there is a total of 40 grams of ice and water in Cup B.

F. Record the temperature of the contents of each cup.

G. Wrap a folded paper towel around the beaker of hot water so you can pick it up without burning your hand. Pour 40 ml of hot water into a graduated cylinder, and place a thermometer in the water. When the temperature has fallen to 80°C, pour the water into Cup A. Stir the mixture carefully for several seconds with a spoon or mixing stick. Record the temperature of the mixture in your notebook.

H. Pour another 40 ml of hot water into the graduated cylinder. When it has cooled to 80°C, pour it into Cup B. Again stir the mixture carefully. As soon as all of the ice has melted, measure the temperature of the mixture and record it in your notebook.

INTERPRETATIONS

1. Compare the final temperatures in Cups A and B. Why are they different?
2. Remember that three phases of matter are solids, liquids, and gases. Predict what would happen to the temperature of boiling water if you added heat energy to it.

PROBLEMS

1. In Procedure G, how many calories of heat were lost by the hot water as it cooled from 80° to the final temperature of the mixture? Remember that 1 calorie is lost by each gram of water for each degree of cooling.
2. In Procedure G, how many calories were gained by the water in Cup A?
3. In Procedure H, how many calories were lost by the hot water after it was poured into Cup B?
4. In Procedure H, how many calories were gained by the ice-and-water mixture in Cup B?
5. How many calories were needed to change each gram of ice to liquid in Procedure H?
6. One pint is equal to approximately 500 ml. If you place a pint of water—at 20°C—in the freezing compartment of a refrigerator, how many calories of heat must the water lose before it freezes?

INVESTIGATION 41: Heat and Volume

MATERIALS (per team)
    Glass tubing (about 60 cm)
    250-ml flask with 1-hole stopper
    Metric ruler
    Burner

PROCEDURES

A. Insert the glass tubing into the hole of the stopper so the tubing will extend about halfway into the flask when the stopper is in position.

B. Put a drop of water in the glass tubing, and let it move down the tubing until it is near the top of the stopper (Figure 11 · 2). Stop the drop by placing a finger over the top end of

Herb Comess

water drop

Figure 11 · 2.
Beginning
Procedure B.

the glass tubing. Keep your finger on the tubing, and seal
the flask with the stopper. Adjust the position of the drop by
pushing down or pulling up on the stopper, so that the bottom
of the drop is slightly above the stopper (Figure 11 · 3).

Herb Comess

Figure 11 · 3.
Completed
set-up for
Procedure B.

water drop

C. Measure and record the distance between the top of the stopper and the drop.
D. Wrap your hands around the flask for several seconds. Measure and record any change in the position of the water drop.
E. Blow the water droplet out of the glass tube. Remove the
stopper and fill the flask to the brim with water. Insert the
stopper into the flask, allowing excess water to spill out. Push
the stopper down until the level of water in the glass tube is
about 20 cm above the top of the stopper. The stopper should
fit firmly in place (Figure 11 · 4).

water level

Herb Comess

Figure 11 · 4.
Set-up for
Procedures E–H.

F. Measure and record the height of the water above the stopper.

G. Wrap your hands around the flask and hold for one minute. Then quickly measure the height of the water column. Record any change in your notebook.

H. Using the burner, gently heat the flask of water for several seconds. Again measure and record any change in the height of the water column.

INTERPRETATIONS

1. In Procedure D, what was responsible for the movement of the water drop?

2. Compare the movement of the water drop in Procedure D with the movement of the water column in Procedures G and H. Remember that molecules in a gas are far apart and attract each other very little, while molecules in a liquid are close together and thus have attraction for each other. Explain the behavior of the water in the glass tube in Procedures D, G, and H by using the kinetic theory of heat.

PROBLEM

1. For what other purpose might you use the tube and flask apparatus?

INVESTIGATION 42: Heat and Molecular Attraction

MATERIALS (per team)
  3 pieces of cotton cloth (1 x 4 inches)
  Rubber bands
  20 ml ditto fluid (alcohol)
  2 beakers
  3 thermometers
  Ring stand and clamps

PROCEDURES

A. Soak one piece of cloth in the ditto fluid; soak the second piece in water; and leave the third piece dry.

B. Remove the piece of cloth from the water, let it drip for about 30 seconds, and wrap it around the bulb of a thermometer. Repeat with the piece of cloth from the ditto fluid, using the second thermometer. Wrap the dry cloth around the third thermometer. Fasten each cloth with a string or a rubber band.

C. Mount the three thermometers on a ring stand, as shown in Figure 11 · 5. Read and record temperatures from each thermometer once per minute for five minutes.

Figure 11 · 5.
Set-up for
Procedure C.

Herb Comess

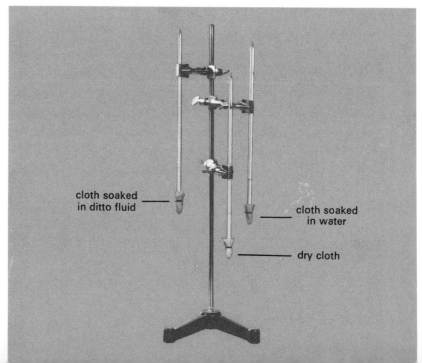

cloth soaked
in ditto fluid _____

cloth soaked _____
in water

_____ dry cloth

INTERPRETATIONS

1. Using the kinetic theory of heat, explain the results of this experiment.
2. What information does this experiment yield about the attraction between alcohol molecules as compared with the attraction between water molecules?

INVESTIGATION 43: Heat Flow

MATERIALS (per team)
Plastic container (about 4 inches across and 5 inches deep)
Aluminum cup (about 2½ inches in diameter and 5 inches deep)
Supply of water at 20°, 50°, and 80°C
Thermometer
Graduated cylinder

PROCEDURES

A. Pour 200 ml of 20°C water into a plastic container, and 200 ml of 50°C water into an aluminum cup. Record the temperatures in your notebook.

B. Put the aluminum cup inside the plastic container as shown in Figure 11 · 6. Take the temperature of the water in the aluminum cup every thirty seconds for five minutes. Record the time and the temperature for each observation. Empty the cup and the plastic container.

Figure 11 · 6.
Set-up for
Procedure B.

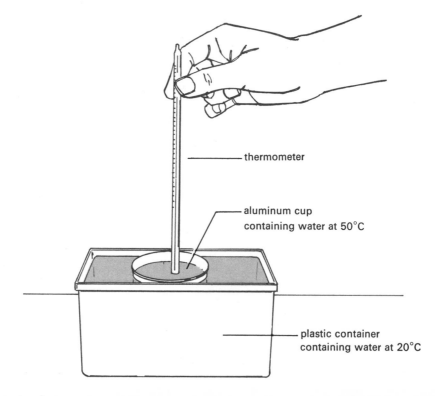

thermometer

aluminum cup
containing water at 50°C

plastic container
containing water at 20°C

C. Repeat Procedures A and B, but pour 80°C water into the plastic container.

INTERPRETATIONS

1. In Investigation 40 you added hot water to cold water and observed the temperature change. What was the experimental purpose of introducing the aluminum cup as a barrier between the samples of water in the present experiment?
2. Does the aluminum cup influence the *direction* of heat flow?
3. How do you suppose the aluminum cup affected the rate of temperature change in the 50° water (as compared to simply mixing the samples of water)? That is, would the rate of temperature change have been faster or slower without the aluminum barrier between the samples?
4. Explain how the aluminum barrier affects the rate of temperature change. Use the kinetic theory of heat in your explanation.
5. How would the rate of temperature change be affected if a plastic cup were used instead of the aluminum cup?

INVESTIGATION 44: Color and Heat

You have gathered information about heat energy. You know heat energy can "flow" through solids and liquids. In molecular terms, heat energy flows through solids and liquids by means of collisions of atoms (or molecules) with other atoms.

There is another way in which heat energy can be transferred, and the next investigation provides an opportunity for you to observe it.

MATERIALS (per team)
> 2 aluminum cans, same shape and size, one painted dull black,
>   the other white (12-oz. soft-drink can)
> 2 thermometers
> Light source (uncovered 150-200 watt bulb)
> Graduated cylinder
> Ruler

PROCEDURES

A. Pour 100 ml of water into each can.
B. Place a thermometer in each can and record the temperatures.
C. Place the cans 10 cm from the *center* of the light bulb, on opposite sides of the bulb (Figure 11 · 7).

Figure 11 · 7.
Set-up for
Procedure C.

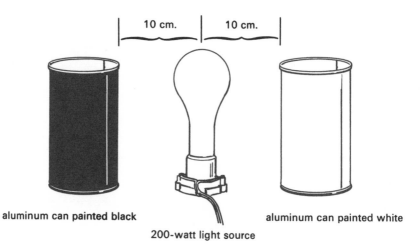

10 cm.   10 cm.

aluminum can painted black   aluminum can painted white

200-watt light source

D. Divide your team into two groups. Each group is responsible for reading and recording temperatures in one of the cans. Readings should be made at the same times by the two groups. Turn on the light, and record the temperature of the water in each can every three minutes. Continue the readings until there is no change in temperatures for three consecutive readings, or until thirty minutes have elapsed.

INTERPRETATIONS

1. How do the final temperatures in the two cans compare?
2. What does the *rate* of temperature change in each can indicate about the rate at which heat flowed into the water?
3. Did heat leave the water? How could you tell?
4. From the position of each can in relation to the heat source, what can you say about the rate at which heat was reaching the cans?
5. Can you use the kinetic theory of heat to explain the results of this experiment?

PROBLEM

1. Explain why many people who live in hot, sunny parts of the country prefer white or other light-colored clothing instead of black clothing.

REFERENCES

Castle, Jack, and others. *Science by Degrees.* New York: Publications Development Corporation (Walker & Co.), 1964.

Cowling, Thomas George. *Molecules in Motion.* New York: Harper and Row, 1960.

Irving, Robert. *Energy and Power.* New York: Alfred A. Knopf, Inc., 1958.

Laver, F. J. M. *Energy.* New York: Oxford University Press, Inc., 1957.

Leerburger, Benedict A., Jr. *Josiah Gibbs: American Theoretical Physicist.* New York: Franklin Watts, Inc., 1963.

Lodge, Sir Oliver Joseph. *Energy.* New York: John F. Rider, Inc., 1957.

MacDonald, D. K. C. *Near Zero: The Physics of Low Temperature.* ("Science Study Series") Garden City, N.Y.: Doubleday & Co., Inc. (Anchor Books), 1964.

Pimentel, G. C. (ed.). *Chemistry: An Experimental Science.* San Francisco: W. H. Freeman and Co., 1963.

Posin, Daniel Q. *What Is Matter.* Chicago: Benefic Press, 1962.

Ruchlis, Hy. *The Wonder of Heat Energy*. New York: Harper and Row, 1961.

Sandfort, John F. *Heat Engines: Thermodynamics in Theory & Practice.* ("Science Study Series") Garden City, N.Y.: Doubleday & Co., Inc. (Anchor Books), 1962.

Sootin, Harry. *Experiments with Heat.* New York: W. W. Norton and Co., Inc., 1964.

Weisskopf, Victor F. *Knowledge and Wonder: The Natural World as Man Knows It.* ("Science Study Series") Garden City, N.Y.: Doubleday & Co., Inc. (Anchor Books), 1963.

Wilson, Mitchell, and the Editors of *Life. Energy.* New York: Time Inc. (Time-Life Books), 1963.

Observing the Behavior of Light

Light, like heat, is a familiar form of energy. Light energy behaves in many different ways. A magnifying glass can focus energy from the sun into a beam that produces enough heat energy to set a piece of paper on fire. Thus light energy and heat energy are apparently related.

Sunlight travels a distance of 93 million miles at a speed of 186,000 miles per second before it strikes the earth. Without sunlight, life could not exist on this planet. Light also affects the behavior of most plants and animals, including man. Most of us, for example, regulate our activity by the sun, working during daylight hours and sleeping during the night. Many kinds of insects are attracted toward light. If you leave a door or window open in your house on a warm summer night, you know that many small insects soon will be flying around the lamps inside. Some insects and other animals move away from light. Early man discovered that the light from his fire would keep wild animals away at night.

A study of the relationships between light and life would require much more time than we have in this course. We will examine some aspects of light and life later, in Section Sixteen.

During the following investigations of light, you will again be asked to construct a model—a model on which to base your understanding of light energy. As you construct the model, consider the following questions: Is sunlight the same kind of light as that given off by a glowing light bulb? How does light travel? What is the relationship between light and color? What causes a rainbow?

Do not attempt to answer these questions now. But keep them in mind as you investigate the phenomenon of light. Perhaps your study will yield some answers to the questions. Also keep in mind that scientists do not completely understand the nature of light. But they continue to study its behavior and to build upon models that may someday reveal much more about light energy than is now known.

INVESTIGATION 45: Observing a Light Beam

MATERIALS (per team)
 Shoe box
 A nail or other pointed object
 Knife or razor blade
 Tape
 Light source (penlight or conductivity-meter light)

PROCEDURES

A. Using a nail, punch a hole about ⅛ inch in diameter in the center of each end of a shoe box and in the center of the box top (see Figure 12 · 1). Punch the holes from the inside out. Trim off any ragged material around the hole with a sharp knife or razor blade. Put the lid on the box and fasten it with a few pieces of tape.

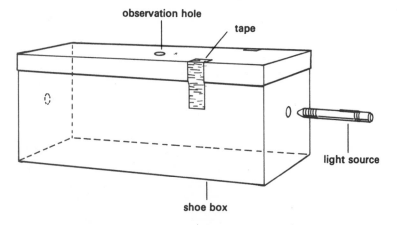

observation hole

tape

light source

shoe box

Figure 12 · 1. Set-up for Procedures A and B

B. Have one member of your team hold the light against the hole in one end of the box. Look into the box through the hole in the opposite end. Then look through the hole in the top of the box. Have each member of your team make these observations.

INTERPRETATIONS

1. Describe and explain any difference in what you saw when looking through the two holes.
2. What appears to be the pathway of light? Verify your answer by shining a flashlight on the wall.
3. Can a light beam be bent so that it will travel around corners?

INVESTIGATION 46: A Model of Light

MATERIALS (per team)
Pocket mirror
Flashlight

PROCEDURE

A. Focus a flashlight beam on a mirror. Hold the mirror at an angle so light striking the mirror will be reflected toward a wall or other solid surface.

INTERPRETATION

1. In what way is the reflection of light from a mirror similar to a ball bouncing against a wall? In what way are these two events not similar? From the results of this investigation, suggest a model that could explain the nature of a light beam.

INVESTIGATION 47: Some Properties of a Mirror

Mirrors are used to study the behavior of light in this investigation and several that follow.

MATERIALS (per class)
Large sheet of white paper
Wall mirror (at least 12 inches square)
Masking tape
Several sheets of tracing paper

MATERIALS (per team)
Sheet of white paper
Pocket-size mirror

PROCEDURES

Note: Procedures A through D should be performed by two students as a demon-stration for the class.

A. Student 1 holds a large sheet of white paper against the chalkboard or a smooth wall. Student 2 stands facing away from the wall, with the back of his head against the paper. Using a pencil, Student 1 should draw an outline of Student 2's head on the paper.

B. Student 2 stands four feet from the large mirror, facing it. Student 1 stands to one side of the mirror and places four small pieces of masking tape on the mirror, outlining Student 2's head *as Student 2 sees it.* Student 1 (following Student 2's instructions) places one piece of masking tape just even with the top of the reflection of Student 2's head, another at the chin, and the others at the ears.

C. Student 1 places a sheet of tracing paper over the tapes on the mirror and draws an outline of the head, using the four pieces of tape as reference points.

D. Compare the two outlines of Student 2's head. Record your observations.

INTERPRETATIONS

1. Which is larger—the outline of the head or the outline of the image?
2. What does this mean for anyone who looks into a mirror?

PROCEDURES (continued)

NOTE: Procedure E is to be performed by each team.

E. Write *TOM* on a sheet of paper. Hold a small mirror so that the letters can be seen as a reflection.

H/W Photographics

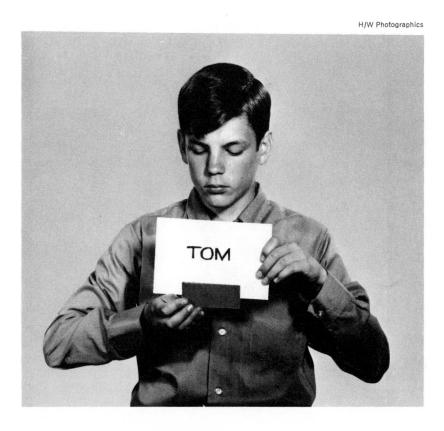

Figure 12 · 2. Carrying out Procedure E.

INTERPRETATIONS (continued)

3. Describe the reflected image.
4. Explain what you observed. If an explanation is difficult at this time, it will be less so after you have performed the next series of investigations.

INVESTIGATION 48: Mirror Reflections

Investigations 48 through 50 introduce additional problems involving the reflection of light from objects viewed in a mirror.

MATERIALS (per student)
    Pocket mirror
    Ruler
    Unruled paper

PROCEDURES

NOTE: In each of the following procedures, place the edge of the mirror along the mirror line (dotted line), as shown in Figure 12 · 3. Always hold the mirror perpendicular to the surface, as shown.

Figure 12 · 3.
Correct position
of the mirror on
the mirror line.

H/W Photographics

A. Hold the mirror on the mirror line in Figure 12 · 4. Where does the diagonal line that extends from the lower *left-hand corner* of the square appear to be in the reflection? Record your answer. Answer the same question for the diagonal line that extends from the lower *right-hand* corner.

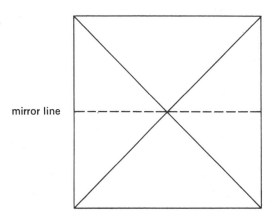

Figure 12 · 4.

B. Hold the mirror on the mirror line in Figure 12 · 5. Where
do the diagonal lines that extend from the corners of the
square appear to be in the reflection? Record your answers.

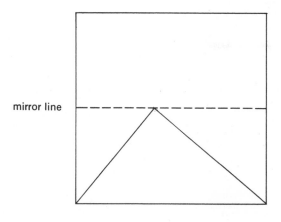

Figure 12 · 5.

C. In your notebook draw a copy of Figure 12 · 6. Draw a line
in the upper half of the square where you think the image of
the line on the lower half of the square would appear.
D. Hold the mirror on the mirror line in Figure 12 · 6. Where
does the image of the diagonal line appear to be in the reflection? Record your observation.

Figure 12 · 6.

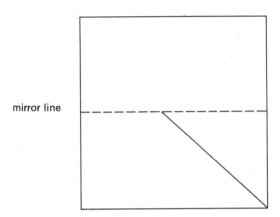

INTERPRETATIONS

1. Did your drawing in Procedure C match the mirror image of the diagonal line in Figure 12 · 6?
2. How are lines reflected in a mirror? Assuming that light is made up of small particles, how would you explain your answer?

INVESTIGATION 49: An Image "Behind" a Mirror

MATERIALS (per team)
    Unruled paper
    Corrugated cardboard (8 x 8 inches)
    Tape
    Several straight pins
    Pocket mirror
    Mirror support

PROCEDURES

A. On a sheet of white paper, draw an enlarged copy of Figure
   12 · 7. The square should be 4 inches on a side. Note that
   points 1 and 2 are equal distances from the edge of the square.
   Tape the sheet of paper to the cardboard.

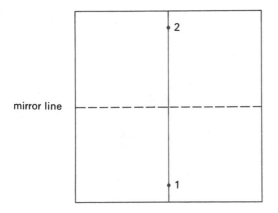

Figure 12 · 7.

B. Insert one pin at point 1 and a second at point 2. Set the
   pins firmly so they stand perpendicular to the paper.
C. Support the mirror so its bottom edge is 2 cm above the paper
   (see Figure 12 · 8). By looking under the mirror you can see
   the lower part of Pin 2 behind the mirror.
D. Look under the mirror. Do you see any relationship between
   the mirror image of Pin 1 and the bottom of Pin 2? View the
   two pins from the left and from the right.

Figure 12 · 8.
Set-up for Procedures C and D.

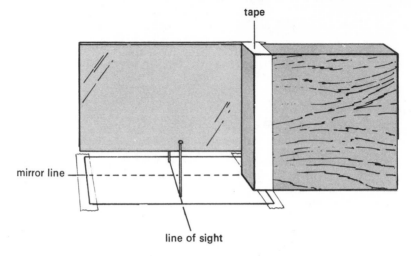

tape

mirror line

line of sight

E. Place Pin 2 at other locations behind the mirror. Observe the relationship of the mirror image of Pin 1 to the bottom of Pin 2.

INTERPRETATIONS

1. Describe what you observed in Procedure D.
2. Did you observe the same effect when the position of Pin 2 was changed?
3. How do these observations compare with the results obtained in Investigations 47 and 48? Compare the distance that an image of an object appears to be "behind" a mirror with the actual distance from the object to the mirror.

INVESTIGATION 50: Comparing Angles Formed When Light Is Reflected

How does the angle at which light strikes a mirror compare with the angle at which the same light is reflected? Finding an answer to this question is the purpose of this investigation.

MATERIALS (per team)
   Unruled paper
   Ruler
   Corrugated cardboard (8 x 8 inches)
   Tape
   4 pins
   Pocket mirror
   Mirror support
   Protractor

PROCEDURES

A. On a sheet of white paper, draw an enlarged copy of Figure 12·9. The square should be 4 inches on a side. Tape the paper to the cardboard.

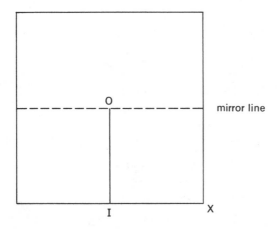

Figure 12 · 9.

B. Draw a line connecting points X and O. Insert two pins about 1 inch apart on line XO.

C. Using the support, place the mirror on the mirror line (see Figure 12 · 10).

Figure 12 · 10.
Set-up for
Procedures C–F.

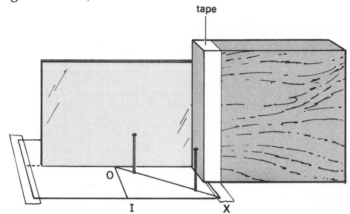

D. Look into the mirror from the left. Move sideways until the images of the two pins line up exactly, one behind the other. Place two more pins on the left side of the paper so that they line up exactly with the images of the first two pins. Remove the mirror. Draw a straight line from the mirror line, through the two new pin points, to the edge of the square.

E. Using a protractor, measure and record (in degrees) first, the angle formed by lines XO and OI, and second, the angle formed by line OI and the line that you added at the end of Procedure D.

INTERPRETATIONS

1. How do the two angles compare?

PROCEDURES (continued)

F. Remove the pins on line XO. Draw a line from some other point on line IX to point O. Place two pins on this line about 2 inches apart. Set the mirror on the mirror line, and repeat Procedures D and E. Repeat, using several other lines; each time, measure the two angles formed by the two sets of pins and line OI.

INTERPRETATIONS (continued)

2. What general statement can you make about the relationship between the angle at which light strikes a mirror and the angle at which light is reflected?
3. Does the behavior of light in this investigation support the particle model of light? Upon what evidence do you base your answer?

INVESTIGATION 51: Behavior of Light Passing Through
Different Substances

MATERIALS (per team)
    Rectangular plastic box with cover
    Wedge-shaped plastic box with cover
    Tape
    Unruled white paper
    Pins
    Corrugated cardboard (8 x 8 inches)
    Ruler

PROCEDURES

A. Fill both plastic containers with water. Put the covers in place, and tape the edges securely to prevent leakage. Dry the outside of each container.

B. Tape a sheet of unruled white paper to the cardboard. Place the rectangular box in the middle of the paper. Draw an outline around the box. Remove the box, and draw a dashed line from just inside the outline to the edge of the paper as shown in Figure 12 · 11.

Figure 12 · 11.
Set-up for
Procedures B–D.

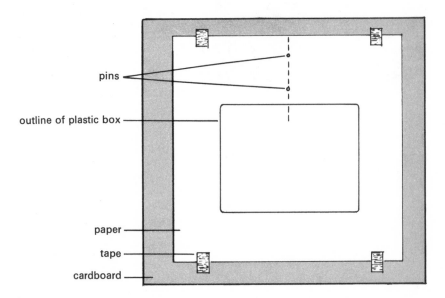

pins

outline of plastic box

paper

tape

cardboard

C. Replace the box in the outline. Insert two pins on the dashed line on one side of the box.

D. Looking *through* the box from the side opposite the two pins, place two more pins on the near side so all four seem to be in a straight line. Remove the box and draw a solid straight line from the top edge of the paper, through the first pair of pins, to the edge of the outline. Draw a second straight line from the bottom edge of the paper, through the second pair of pins, to the edge of the outline. Draw a third straight line connecting the points at which the two lines meet the outline.

INTERPRETATIONS

1. Are the four pins in a straight line?
2. Describe the pathway of light as it travels from air, through water, and into air. (Light reflected from the pins must follow this path when you look at them through the water.)

PROCEDURES (continued)

E. Place the box in the outline again, and insert the two pins as shown in Figure 12 · 12.

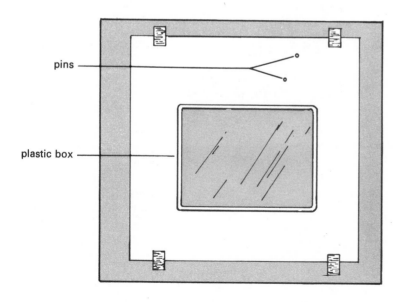

pins

plastic box

Figure 12 · 12. Set-up for Procedures E and F.

F. Look *through* the box from the side opposite the pins, and place two more pins on the near side, so all four seem to be in a straight line. Remove the box and draw a solid straight line from the top edge of the paper, through the first pair of pins, to the edge of the outline. Draw a second straight line from the bottom edge of the paper, through the second pair of pins, to the edge of the outline. Draw a third straight line connecting the points at which the two lines meet the outline.

INTERPRETATIONS (continued)

3. Compare the results of Procedures D and F.
4. Earlier you found evidence that light travels in a straight line. If this is so, how can you explain the results obtained in Procedure F?

PROCEDURES (continued)

G. Place the wedge-shaped box of water on a clean piece of white paper on the cardboard, and draw an outline of its shape. Insert two pins as shown in Figure 12 · 13.

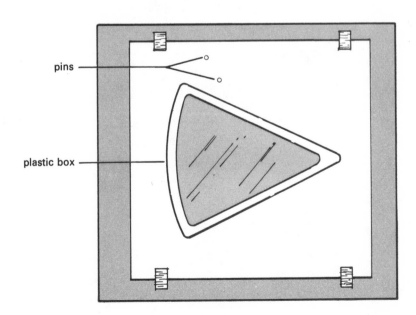

Figure 12 · 13. Set-up for Procedures G and H.

pins

plastic box

H. Look *through* the box from the side opposite the two pins. Place two more pins on the near side so all four seem to be in a straight line. Remove the box and draw a solid straight line from the top edge of the paper, through the first pair of pins, to the edge of the outline. Draw a second straight line from the bottom edge of the paper, through the second pair of pins, to the edge of the outline. Draw a third straight line connecting the points at which the two lines meet the outline.

INTERPRETATIONS (continued)

5. Describe the lines you drew in Procedure H. How do they compare with the lines drawn in Procedures D and F?
6. How can your model of light energy—from which we assume that light travels in straight lines—be made to agree with the results of Procedure H?

Another Look at a Model of Light

You know that moving particles possess energy. In many instances, the behavior of light can be explained with a particle model.

We can predict that when light strikes a smooth surface, such as the surface of a pond or a mirror, the light will bounce off (be reflected) and travel in a different direction. Almost every investigation of light you have performed makes a particle model of light seem reasonable. And the idea that light energy is composed of particles is often used by modern scientists to explain the behavior of light.

But how can we explain the bending of light when it passes from air into water and back into air? And why does light bend in different directions, depending upon the shape of the container and the angle at which light strikes the container? It is difficult to imagine how a particle could behave in this way. An alternative model of light will be investigated next, in Section Thirteen. After completing all the investigations involving light, you should be able to refine your model so that every observation you make can be explained in terms of your model.

REFERENCES

Asimov, Isaac. *Breakthroughs in Science.* Boston: Houghton Mifflin Co., 1959.

Beeler, Nelson F., and Branley, F. M. *Experiments in Optical Illusions.* New York: The Thomas Y. Crowell Co., 1951.

Newton, Sir Isaac. *Opticks or a Treatise of the Reflections, Refractions, Inflections and Colours of Light.* New York: Dover Publications, Inc., 1952.

Pierce, John R. *Electrons and Waves: An Introduction to the Science of Electronics & Communication.* ("Science Study Series") Garden City, N.Y.: Doubleday & Co., Inc. (Anchor Books), 1964.

Sandfort, John F. *Heat Engines: Thermodynamics in Theory & Practice.* ("Science Study Series") Garden City, N.Y.: Doubleday & Co., Inc. (Anchor Books), 1962.

Sootin, Harry. *Isaac Newton.* New York: Simon & Schuster (Julien Messner Inc.), 1955.

Weisskopf, Victor F. *Knowledge and Wonder: The Natural World as Man Knows It.* ("Science Study Series") Garden City, N.Y.: Doubleday & Co., Inc. (Anchor Books), 1963.

Observing the Nature of Waves

Huge ocean waves, created by winds or earthquakes, often cause great damage to coastal areas, destroying both property and lives. Wave action and tides gradually erode land exposed to these forces.

It may be that wave action is a form of energy, and that waves carry energy. Perhaps you live a great distance from an ocean or large lake and cannot observe the behavior of waves. But you can create ripples in a dish of water and investigate wave action on a small scale. The behavior of water waves may provide you with ideas for another model for the behavior of light.

In the following investigations, the behavior of waves in the ripple tank will be demonstrated. You are to observe each demonstration and record your observations. From your notes you will be asked to describe a general model of wave action that might explain the behavior of water waves and the behavior of light.

Figure 13 · 1. The force of waves pounding against a rocky shore is an example of natural energy at work.

INVESTIGATION 52: Mirrors and Wave Action

In this investigation a piece of metal is used as a mirror to reflect water waves—just as an ordinary mirror reflects light.

MATERIALS (per class)
 Ripple tank with wave generator
 Overhead projector
 Pointed object (pencil)
 Metal "mirrors"

PROCEDURES
A. Observe the shape and motion of waves created when the water in the tank is disturbed with a pointed object. Record your observations.
B. A flat metal mirror has been placed in front of the ripple tank wave generator. When a pointed object disturbs the water, observe and record the appearance of waves as they are reflected from the mirror.
C. Unlike the pointed object, the wave generator creates waves along a broad front. Observe and record the appearance of these waves as they are reflected by the metal mirror.

INTERPRETATIONS
1. Compare the amount of wave motion present between the wave generator and the mirror with the wave motion present *behind* the mirror.

PROCEDURES (continued)
D. The metal mirror has been placed at an angle of about 45° in the ripple tank. Observe and record the direction of the *reflected* waves.
E. Now a curved mirror has been placed in the ripple tank. Observe and record the appearance of the reflected waves.

INTERPRETATIONS (continued)
2. Predict how light would behave when reflected from a curved mirror shaped like the one used in Procedure E.

INVESTIGATION 53: Changing the Direction of Wave Travel

MATERIALS (per class)
Ripple tank with generator
Triangular metal "prism"
Round metal "lens"

PROCEDURES

A. A triangular metal prism has been placed in front of the ripple tank wave generator. Carefully observe and record any change in the direction of waves as they move beyond the "prism."
B. The metal prism has been replaced by a round metal "lens." Observe and record any change in the direction of the waves as they move over and beyond the lens.

INTERPRETATION

1. Compare changes in direction observed in water waves with the bending of light passing from one substance to another (see Investigation 52).

INVESTIGATION 54: Interference of Water Waves

The term *interference* is used to describe what happens when several waves meet and form new patterns.

MATERIALS (per class)
> Ripple tank with generator
> Interference plate
> Masking tape

PROCEDURES

A. Observe wave action that results from a point source.

B. Now observe wave interference, as waves generated from two different points meet. Record your observations. If necessary, draw a diagram in your notebook that represents the effect of wave interference.

C. An interference plate has been placed in the ripple tank. The plate is similar to a metal mirror, except that an opening has been cut in it, allowing waves to pass through at one point. Observe and record the appearance of waves as they strike the plate and travel through the opening.

D. Now there are two openings in the interference plate. Observe and record the interference patterns as waves come together after passing through the two openings.

INTERPRETATIONS

1. Compare the pattern of waves formed by a single opening in the interference plate (Procedure C) with the pattern of waves formed by a pointed object (Procedure A).

2. Compare the interference patterns formed by the merging waves that have passed through the two openings (Procedure D) with the merging waves formed by pointed objects at two locations (Procedure B).

INVESTIGATION 55: Viewing Light Through Small Openings

You have observed interference patterns in water waves. You have also observed that light and water waves are reflected and bent in similar ways. Although there appear to be similarities between water waves and light, there are also differences. For example, you have never seen light move up and down like the water waves in a ripple tank. But you might be able to see a pattern of energy distribution for light that resembles the energy distribution for water waves. Copy Figure 13 · 2 in your notebook. Fill in the blank spaces by describing the amount of light you would expect for each amount of energy.

Figure 13 · 2.

	ENERGY			
	None	*Small amount*	*Moderate amount*	*Large amount*
Water	Calm	Rippled	Waves	Large Waves
Light				

MATERIALS (per student)
    Light source
    Aluminum foil with two small openings
    Diffraction grating

PROCEDURES
A. Handle the aluminum foil with care; it tears easily. Examine it carefully. You will find two very small openings, about 1 mm apart, in the foil. What do you think you would see if you were to view a light source through the two openings? Would you see two beams of light? one beam of light? *Do not perform Procedure B until you have recorded your prediction.*
B. Hold the foil at arm's length between your eyes and the light source. You may be able to see the two openings. Now bring the foil close to one eye, so that the two openings appear to blend into one. Rotate the foil while looking at the light through the openings.

INTERPRETATIONS

1. Describe what you observed through the openings while holding the foil close to one eye. Did you predict the result correctly? .

2. Suggest an explanation for your observations. Relate your explanation to what you know about water waves.

3. Can your observations be explained with a particle model of light?

PROCEDURES (continued)

C. The diffraction grating has many openings so small and so close together that you cannot see them. The openings are narrow slits in the plastic film. There are 13,400 slits per inch! What do you think you would see if you were to look at the light source through the diffraction grating? Do not perform Procedure D until you have recorded your prediction.

D. Hold the diffraction grating close to your eye, and look at the light source. Then look slightly to the left or right of the light source to see the effect produced by the diffraction grating.

INTERPRETATIONS (continued)

4. Did your observation agree with your prediction?

5. Describe as accurately as possible what you observed.

REFERENCES

Adler, Irving. *The Secret of Light.* New York: International Publishers Co., Inc., 1952.

Bascom, Willard. *Waves and Beaches: The Dynamics of the Ocean Surface.* ("Science Study Series") Garden City, N.Y.: Doubleday & Co., Inc. (Anchor Books), 1960.

Benade, Arthur H. *Horns, Strings and Harmony.* ("Science Study Series") Garden City, New York: Doubleday Anchor, 1960.

Bixby, William G. *Waves: Pathways of Energy.* New York: David McKay Co., 1963.

Davis, Kenneth S., and Day, John A. *Water: the Mirror of Science.* ("Science Study Series") Garden City, N.Y.: Doubleday & Co., Inc. (Anchor Books), 1961.

Griffin, Donald R. *Echoes of Bats and Men.* ("Science Study Series") Garden City, N.Y.: Doubleday & Co., Inc. (Anchor Books), 1959.

Jaffe, Bernard. *Michelson and the Speed of Light.* ("Science Study Series") Garden City, N.Y.: Doubleday & Co., Inc. (Anchor Books), 1960.

PSSC. *Physics.* Boston: D.C. Heath & Co., 1965.

Pimentel, G. C. (ed.). *Chemistry: An Experimental Science.* San Francisco: W. H. Freeman and Co., 1963.

Roller, Duane E. *Early Development of the Concepts of Temperature and Heat.* Cambridge, Mass.: Harvard University Press, 1950.

Ruchlis, Hyman. *The Wonder of Light.* New York: Harper and Row, 1960.

Ruechardt, Eduard. *Light: Visible and Invisible.* Ann Arbor, Mich.: University of Michigan Press, 1958.

Tannenbaum, Beulah, and Stillman, Myra. *Understanding Light: The Science of Visible and Invisible Rays.* New York: McGraw-Hill Book Co., 1960.

Van Bergeijk, Willem A. M., and others. *Waves and the Ear.* ("Science Study Series") Garden City, N.Y.: Doubleday & Co., Inc. (Anchor Books), 1960.

Wilson, Mitchell, and the Editors of *Life. Energy.* New York: Time Inc. (Time-Life Books), 1963.

Energy Conversion

As you have seen, the behavior of light is complex. White light passing through a diffraction grating acts, in some respects, like water waves. But white light reflected from a mirror behaves more like a stream of particles.

Now you are to investigate the reflection of light from surfaces having different colors.

INVESTIGATION 56: Color—Reflection and Absorption

Why do objects appear to have different colors? How is color related to a model of light? To examine these and other questions is the purpose of this investigation.

MATERIALS (per team)

Viewing box with light source and filter holder (Figure 14·1)

Colored filters (red, blue, green, and yellow)

Colored squares mounted on black paper (Figure 14·2)

To construct the viewing box shown in Figure 14 · 1, the following materials will be needed:

Shoe box

Cardboard packing box (about 2 feet on each side)

110-volt light socket, cord, and plug

110-volt, 25-watt unfrosted light bulb

Masking tape

4 sheets of colored cellophane (red, blue, green, and yellow)

4 pieces of cardboard (6 x 9 inches)

Sharp knife

Figure 14 · 1. Diagram showing how to construct viewing box and filter holder.

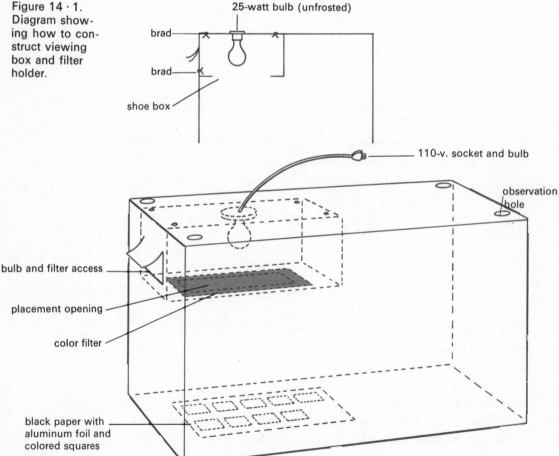

The box is designed so that a variety of color samples can be examined with white light and with light that has passed through colored filters. The bottom of the large box should be open, so the black paper with colored squares (or other objects) can be placed in position for viewing. *Check with your instructor before connecting the light source to an electrical outlet.*

Each piece of cardboard should be large enough to cover the opening in the bottom of the shoe box. Cut a hole 4 x 6 inches in each piece of cardboard and in the bottom of the shoe box. Fasten colored cellophane over each cardboard frame with tape.

Cut the flap allowing access to the bulb after you have assembled the two boxes. Finally, cut the opening for the bulb socket and insert the bulb through the access flap. Fasten 1-inch squares of colored paper and aluminum foil to a piece of black paper (10 x 4 inches) as shown in Figure 14 · 2.

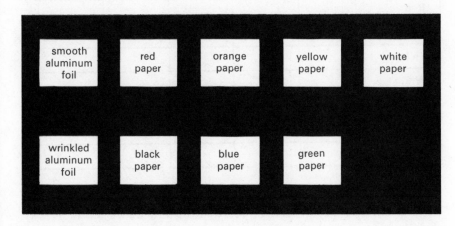

Figure 14 · 2. Black paper with aluminum foil and colored squares to be used in the viewing box

PROCEDURES

A. Place the black paper with squares under the viewing box, as shown in Figure 14 · 1. *Before* performing Procedure B, predict which of the two aluminum squares will appear brighter when viewed under white light.

B. View each of the squares under the white light. Have each member of the team look through all of the observation holes. Record the appearance and color of each square.

INTERPRETATIONS

1. Which appears brighter—the smooth aluminum foil, or the wrinkled foil? From your model of light, explain the appearance of the two aluminum squares.
2. Do the pieces of colored paper appear to change color when viewed in the box?

PROCEDURES (continued)

C. Place the red filter over the opening in the shoe box. Observe and record the appearance of each colored square. Repeat with each of the other filters, recording your observation in a table similar to the one shown in Figure 14 · 3.

Figure 14 · 3.

Color of Paper Square	Color of Paper Squares Under Filtered Light				
	No Filter	Red Filter	Blue Filter	Green Filter	Yellow Filter
Red					
Orange					
Yellow					
White					
Black					
Blue					
Green					

INTERPRETATIONS (continued)

3. Explain the observations recorded in Procedure C.

INVESTIGATION 57: Color and Chemicals

Some chemical compounds have distinct colors. Others are white or colorless. In this investigation heat energy will be added to several chemicals.

MATERIALS (per team)
    Burner (gas or alcohol)

MATERIALS (per class)
    9 nichrome wire flame testers
    Small amounts of each of the following crystals:
        Copper chloride ($CuCl_2$)
        Copper nitrate $Cu(NO_3)_2$
        Copper sulfate ($CuSO_4$)
        Potassium chloride (KCl)
        Potassium bromide (KBr)
        Potassium sulfate (K_2SO_4)
        Sodium chloride (NaCl)
        Sodium bromide (NaBr)
        Sodium sulfate (Na_2SO_4)

PROCEDURES

A. Label each of the nichrome wire flame testers with the name of one of the chemicals to be tested. Each chemical must be used *only* with the tester carrying its name.

CAUTION: *Keep your eyes as far as possible from the flame when testing the chemicals. Wear goggles if possible. The crystals may shatter and cause injury.*

B. Place one or more crystals of a chemical in the loop at the end of the nichrome wire. Hold the loop near the tip of the burner flame until the crystals are used up (see Figure 14 · 4). Observe the color of the flame. Record your observation on a table similar to the one shown in Figure 14 · 5.

Figure 14 · 4.
Set-up for Pro-
cedures B and C.

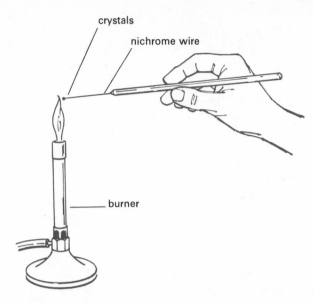

C. Exchange nichrome wire testers and chemicals with other teams. Continue testing until all teams have observed the heating of each chemical.

Figure 14 · 5.

Chemical	Color of Flame
$CuCl_2$	
$Cu(NO_3)_2$	
$CuSO_4$	
KCl	
KBr	
K_2SO_4	
NaCl	
NaBr	
Na_2SO_4	

INTERPRETATIONS

1. Can you find any relationships between flame colors and the chemical formulas?

2. Which ion in each of the chemicals tested appears to be responsible for the flame color given off by that chemical?

3. What do you think is the source of energy that produced the color change?
4. Develop a model that could explain the color changes. Include evidence gathered from previous investigations to support your model.
5. See Figure 14·6 (color insert).

Energy Conversion and Electricity

Most of us take for granted the electrical energy used to light our homes and run electrical appliances. Giant hydroelectric and steam generating plants convert the kinetic energy of moving water and the stored energy of fuels into electricity for use in homes and industry.

Flashlights and portable appliances are powered by batteries. In them, electrical energy must be converted from some other form of energy. It is convenient to transport energy in the form of electricity, and then reconvert it into light energy, mechanical energy, heat energy, and other forms of energy useful to man.

You have already studied many aspects of energy conversion and have attempted to develop models that explain the results of your investigations. You will examine some additional features of energy conversion in the next series of investigations. Though each investigation is different, the results of each can be explained using the models you have already constructed. Figure $14 \cdot 7A$, B, and C, illustrate one form of energy conversion.

INVESTIGATION 58: Electricity and Light

You have seen how electrical energy can be converted into light energy (Investigation 56, page 253). This investigation will focus on a related (but different) form of energy conversion.

MATERIALS (per team)
  Silicon solar cell
  Milliammeter
  Light source (unfrosted 25-watt showcase bulb with a long
    element)

PROCEDURE
A. Hold the silicon solar cell so that it faces the light source (see Figure $14 \cdot 8$). Observe the movement of the milliammeter

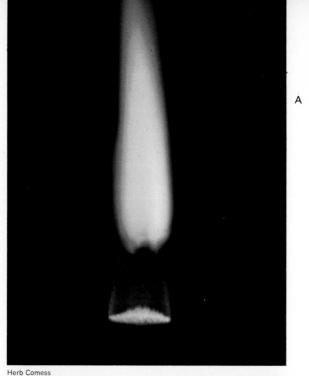

A

B

Figure 14·6. The light emitted by each of these three flames has a color characteristic of the elements present. From the results of Investigation 57, can you tell which flame was produced by N_aCl, by $Cu(NO_3)_2$, and by KCl?

C

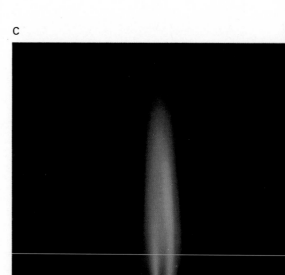

A

B

C

Figure 14·7. What form of energy conversion is being illustrated by these three photographs? How is the color of light related to the voltage?

needle. Vary the distance from the solar cell to the light source, and record your observations.

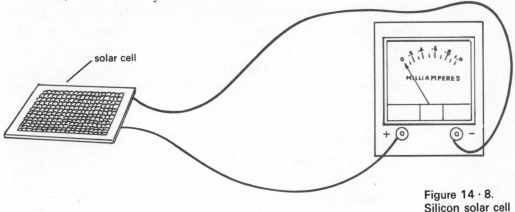

Figure 14 · 8.
Silicon solar cell
and milliammeter.

INTERPRETATIONS

1. The needle indicates the flow of current—or, to be more exact, electrons—through the meter. What is the source of these electrons?

2. When no light strikes the solar cell, no electrons flow through the meter. When light shines on the solar cell, energy moves the electrons. Where does this energy come from?

3. What practical value might solar cells have in modern industry or scientific research?

INVESTIGATION 59: Heat and Electricity

Another form of energy conversion can be illustrated by heating two different metals that are connected to a meter. As you carry out this investigation, try to relate the energy effects to your model of the structure of matter. Your final goal is to understand the relationship of matter and energy. To do this you must work your knowledge of energy into your atomic model.

MATERIALS (per team)
Alcohol burner

Candle

Copper wire

Nichrome wire

Matches

Milliammeter

PROCEDURE
A. Twist the ends of the bare copper wire and the nichrome wire together tightly (10 to 15 turns) as shown in Figure 14 · 9. Connect the free end of the copper wire to the *positive* terminal of the meter. Connect the free end of the nichrome

Figure 14 · 9.
Set-up for
Procedure A.

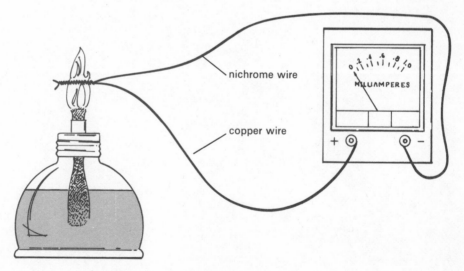

wire to the *negative* terminal. Hold the twisted ends of the wires over the flame of an alcohol burner. Heat the wires to red hot. Observe and record any movement of the meter indicator in your notebook.

B. Hold the twisted ends of the wire in the flame of a candle. Record the meter reading.

C. List some other sources of heat you would like to test with the twisted wires. Check with your teacher before you try them.

INTERPRETATIONS

1. Explain, in terms of electrical energy, the effect of heating two different kinds of metal that are touching.

2. Suggest a use for devices such as the one used in this investigation. (The current generated is not sufficient to operate a light bulb or an electric motor.)

INVESTIGATION 60: Chemical Potential Energy

Stored chemical energy may be released by causing chemicals to react. Natural gas reacts with oxygen, releasing heat and light. Anhydrous copper sulfate reacts with water, producing heat. Gasoline combines with air in an engine, supplying energy.

In chemical reactions electrons are rearranged, and some of the stored energy is released.

MATERIALS (per team)
Paper toweling
2 test tubes (15 x 120 mm)
50 ml of 1 molar copper-sulfate solution
Copper wire
50 ml of 1 molar iron-chloride solution
Iron wire
Milliammeter
Graduated cylinder (100 ml)
Metric ruler
Scissors

PROCEDURES

A. Pour the copper-sulfate solution into one of the test tubes. Put one end of the copper wire into this solution. Pour the iron-chloride solution into the other tube. Put one end of the iron wire into this solution. Label the tubes.

B. Connect the iron wire to the negative pole of the meter. Connect the copper wire to the positive pole of the meter. Observe the meter.

C. Cut a strip of paper toweling about 6 cm wide and about 16 cm long. Fold it in half (lengthwise) three times so that its final width is less than 1 cm. Bend it into a U-shape. Insert one end of the paper toweling into the copper-sulfate solution. Insert the other end into the iron-chloride solution. (See Figure 14 · 10.)

When the toweling is completely wet, observe and record the meter reading.

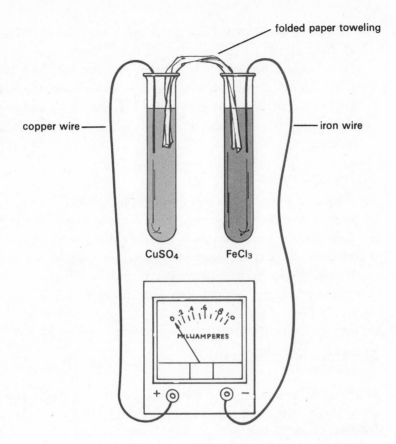

folded paper toweling

copper wire —————   ————— iron wire

CuSO₄   FeCl₃

Figure 14 · 10.
Set-up for
Procedure C.

D. To find out how concentration affects the reaction, you will
   need to dilute the solutions. Pour 10 ml of 1-molar iron-chloride
   solution into the graduated cylinder. Add enough distilled
   water to make 100 ml of solution. Remove and discard the
   paper toweling connecting the two test tubes. Remove the
   iron wire from the test tube. Empty the test tube containing
   iron chloride and refill it with the diluted solution. Put the
   iron wire back into the test tube containing dilute iron chloride. Repeat Procedure C, and record the meter reading.
E. Rinse the graduated cylinder. Pour 10 ml of 1-molar copper-
   sulfate solution into the graduated cylinder. Add enough distilled water to make 100 ml of solution.

Remove and discard the paper toweling used in Procedure D. Remove the wires from the test tubes. Empty the test tubes. Pour 1-molar iron-chloride solution into the test tube labeled *iron chloride,* and replace the iron wire. Pour the diluted copper-sulfate solution into the other test tube, and replace the copper wire. Repeat Procedure C, and record the meter reading.

INTERPRETATIONS

1. Electrical energy is being generated, as shown by the movement of the meter indicator. What is the source of this energy?
2. Can you suggest a practical use for this apparatus?
3. (Optional). Explain the difference in results for Procedures D and E. In your explanation include a discussion of the reaction between copper ions and electrons.

Electromagnetic Energy

White light seems to be a combination of all colors. You saw these colors when you looked at a white light through a diffraction grating. The energy that comes from a source of light is not limited to the kind of energy you can see. Heat is given off by a flame or an electric light. On a cloudy day it is possible to get a sunburn even though you feel cool. Visible light and the kinds of energy that produce warmth and sunburn are examples of electromagnetic energy.

The sun is 93 million miles from the earth. Yet we can use energy from the sun because electromagnetic energy travels through space.

Many other kinds of energy are also types of electromagnetic energy. All these are shown in the electromagnetic spectrum (Figure 14·11). Radio, television, and radar signals travel from transmitters to receivers as low-energy electromagnetic waves. Infrared radiation is an electromagnetic wave. When it is absorbed by matter, heat is produced. Waves of infrared and visible light have more energy than waves of radio, television, or radar. Ultraviolet rays and X-rays are electromagnetic waves with even greater amounts of energy. Infrared radiation is used in cooking food and heating buildings. Sunlight and electric lights are part of our requirements for normal living. Ultraviolet radiation is useful in killing certain disease organisms. X-rays and gamma rays have so much energy that they travel right through solid objects. They can be used to detect and treat cancer. X-rays are used in industry to find hidden cracks in metal, and in medicine to reveal broken bones.

Usually we use electricity to generate electromagnetic energy. The source of most of our energy is the sun. Heat from the sun causes water to evaporate. When the water falls to the earth, as rain, some of it is trapped behind dams and then used to operate electric generators. Other generators are powered by coal. But the energy stored in coal came from the sun, too.

Until recently, the source of the tremendous amount of energy

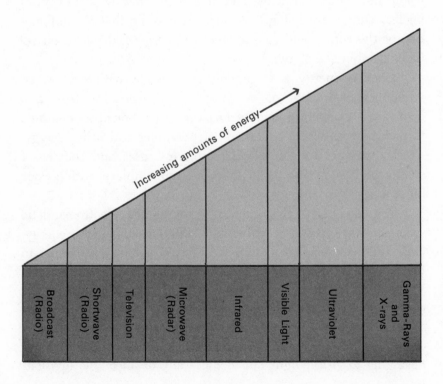

Figure 14 · 11. The electromagnetic spectrum. When electromagnetic energy interacts with matter, work is done. The kind of interaction depends on the amount of energy involved. When an X-ray or a gamma ray strikes matter, a relatively large amount of energy is released. When a radio wave strikes matter, a much smaller amount of energy is released. The electromagnetic energy spectrum is a continuous series of energies —from the very small amount in a radio wave to the large amount in a gamma ray.

Increasing amounts of energy

Broadcast (Radio)

Shortwave (Radio)

Television

Microwave (Radar)

Infrared

Visible Light

Ultraviolet

Gamma-Rays and X-rays

given off by the sun was a puzzle. If the sun depended on chemical reactions, it would have used up all its energy long ago. Experiments with electromagnetic radiation led to the theory that mass can be converted into energy. About forty years after the theory was proposed, nuclear energy was harnessed by man. Chemical energy comes from electron rearrangements. Nuclear energy comes from a change in the nucleus of an atom. Compared with chemical reactions, nuclear reactions release millions of times more energy per pound of fuel. We now believe that the sun's energy comes from the nuclear reactions in which hydrogen is changed into helium.

There are advantages and disadvantages in using nuclear energy. Whenever nuclear reactions take place, high-energy electromagnetic radiation is released. This radiation can have harmful effects on living things. Nuclear power plants are surrounded by heavy shielding to absorb this radiation. If heavy protective shielding were not needed, airplanes and land vehicles would now be powered by nuclear energy. New ways to control nuclear energy are being developed. It may be that the automobile of the future will run on nuclear energy and will need refueling only once or twice a year.

Nuclear energy is beginning to compete with coal as an economical source of power to generate electricity. It is also being used to operate engines in large ships. Scientists continue to seek new and better methods of obtaining and using energy. At the present rate of scientific progress, uses and sources of energy undreamed of today may be commonplace within your lifetime.

You have seen that each division of the electromagnetic spectrum is composed of waves with different amounts of energy. Only those waves that can be seen by the naked eye belong to the division of the electromagnetic spectrum called visible light. Violet light produces the shortest waves that can be seen by the naked eye. Ultraviolet light and X-rays produce waves even shorter than violet light, but these are not visible to the naked eye. Therefore, the term *spectrum* is not limited to those waves belonging to visible light but includes any or all of the divisions of the electromagnetic spectrum.

All spectra can be broken down into lesser divisions and these, in turn, can be subdivided into what are known as continuous and bright line spectra. Examples of the first two of these subdivisions are shown in Figure 14·12.

REFERENCES

Adler, Irving. *Color in Your Life.* New York: The John Day Company, Inc., 1962.

Battan, Louis J. *Radar Observes the Weather.* ("Science Study Series") Garden City, New York: Doubleday Anchor, 1962.

Jaffe, Bernard. *Michelson and the Speed of Light.* ("Science Study Series") Garden City, New York: Doubleday Anchor, 1960.

Pimental, G. C. (ed.). *Chemistry an Experimental Science.* San Francisco: W. H. Freeman & Co., 1963.

Romer, Alfred S. *The Restless Atom.* ("Science Study Series") Garden City New York: Doubleday Anchor, 1960.

Weisskopf, Victor F. *Knowledge and Wonder: The Natural World as Man Knows It.* ("Science Study Series") Garden City, New York: Doubleday Anchor, 1963.

Wilson, Mitchell, and eds. of Life Magazine. *Energy.* New York: Time-Life Books, a division of Time, Inc., 1963.

Bright line
spectrum of
hydrogen.

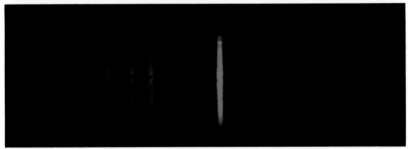

Bright line
spectrum of
mercury.

Bright line
spectrum of
helium.

Figure 14·12. When white light is bent with a diffraction grating, a
rectangle appears that is made up of a pattern of colors. None of
these colors is white. Red light appears at one end of the rectangle
and violet light at the other, with a continuous sequence of colors in
between. An unbroken spectrum of colors, such as this, is called a
continuous spectrum.

When light from glowing gases such as hydrogen, mercury, and helium
passes through a diffraction grating a *bright line spectrum* results.
Bright line spectra are composed of distinct and separate color lines.
These lines of colors are "fingerprints" that identify the gas present.
Are the colors that appear in each of the bright line spectra, shown
in this figure, also present in the continuous spectrum?

Some Chemical Reactions in Living and Non-Living Things

You have been studying the interaction of energy and non-living matter. Various forms of energy have been investigated—electrical, chemical, light, gravitational, and heat.

You will now investigate some of the relationships of matter and energy in *living* things, and you will be asked to compare these with some reactions in non-living systems. Energy is required to produce motion; so you know energy is needed if an animal is to walk, run, or fly. You have also learned that energy is involved in chemical reactions. Many kinds of chemical reactions take place in living things, and, like all chemical reactions, these involve energy.

You might observe some of the activities of living things, but your observations would not explain *how* energy is used or from *where* it is obtained. The more you learn about the interaction of matter and energy in living things, the better you will understand man's need to conserve the energy vital to all life. The supply of useful energy on earth is limited, and we are using it up at a rapidly increasing rate.

INVESTIGATION 61: Reactions in a Yeast Culture

Yeasts are very tiny plants related to toadstools, mushrooms, molds, and other plants called *fungi*. Because yeast reproduces rapidly, it is ideal for many laboratory studies.

MATERIALS (per team)
> 2 calibrated thermometers
> 2 quart jars
> 500 ml of molasses-water mixture
> 2 thermos bottles with stoppers
> 25 ml of 15% formalin solution
> 10 ml of yeast-water mixture
> Cotton or Kleenex

PROCEDURES

A. Place the thermometers in a jar filled with water for two minutes. Take the temperature reading from each thermometer. If there is a difference in the readings, number the thermometers and make a note of the difference for future reference.

B. Pour the molasses-water mixture into two thermos bottles until each is about three-fourths full. Pour 25 ml of formalin solution into one of the thermos bottles, and label the bottle *Formalin/Yeast/Molasses.* Pour 25 ml of water into the second thermos bottle and label it *Yeast/Molasses.*

CAUTION: *Formalin is injurious to the skin. Avoid spilling it on your hands.*

C. Pour 5 ml of yeast-water mixture into each thermos bottle. Stopper each bottle and shake thoroughly.

D. Remove the stoppers. Prepare two plugs large enough to stopper the thermos bottles by wrapping cotton or folded Kleenex around the stems of the two thermometers. Insert the thermometers and plugs into each thermos bottle, as shown in Figure 15 · 1. Adjust each thermometer so the bulb is below the surface of the liquid.

E. In your notebook copy the chart shown in Figure 15 · 2. After the bottles have been plugged for about five minutes, slide the

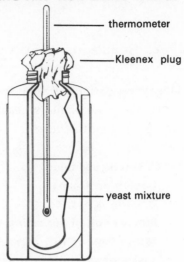

thermometer

Kleenex plug

yeast mixture

Figure 15 · 1.
Set-up for
Procedure D.

thermometers up through the plugs. Take readings, and lower the thermometers to their original position.

Figure 15 · 2.

| Date | Time | Temperature in Degrees Centigrade | |
		Yeast/Molasses	Formalin/Yeast/Molasses

Record the temperature in each bottle, the date, and the time of day on the chart. Take several readings from the two thermometers on each of the next few days. During this time both bottles should be kept in the same place, out of direct sunlight and away from any source of heat or cold.

INTERPRETATIONS

1. Explain any difference in temperature in the two bottles. In your explanation, describe the effect of adding formalin to one bottle.
2. What can you say about energy in a growing yeast population?

INVESTIGATION 62: Reactions in Sprouting Seeds

This investigation is similar to Investigation 61, but here sprouting seeds of a green plant (wheat) are used instead of a population of non-green plants (yeast).

MATERIALS (per team)

    Cotton or Kleenex
    2 thermos bottles
    Pint jar full of sprouting wheat grains
    100–200 ml of 15% formalin solution (amount depends on
       size of thermos bottles)
    2 calibrated thermometers
    Pans (or ready access to sink)

Figure 15 · 3.
Set-up for
Procedure E.

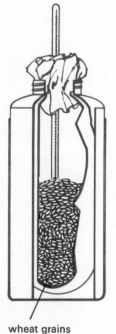

wheat grains

PROCEDURES

A. Place several sheets of wet Kleenex in the bottom of each thermos bottle. Pour sprouting wheat grains into both bottles, until they are about two-thirds full.

B. Add enough water to one bottle to cover the wheat grains. Label this bottle *Wheat/Water*. Set the bottle aside for about thirty minutes. Add enough of the formalin solution to the second bottle to cover the grains. Label this bottle *Wheat/Formalin*, and set it aside for about thirty minutes.

CAUTION: *Formalin is injurious to the skin. Avoid spilling it on your hands.*

C. Make two plugs by wrapping cotton or Kleenex around the stem of each thermometer (as in the previous investigation).

D. After thirty minutes, pour the water and formalin—but not the grains—from the two bottles into pans or the sink. Hold a stopper loosely over the mouth of each bottle to keep the grains from falling out. (Use a cork or solid stopper, not the cotton plugs.)

CAUTION: *Avoid getting formalin on your hands. If you do, wash it off immediately.*

E. Insert a thermometer and a cotton or Kleenex plug into each of the two bottles, as shown in Figure 15 · 3. Adjust the thermometers so the bulbs are near the middle of the mass of wheat grains. Wait about five minutes, and then take a reading from each thermometer. Record the temperatures, date, and the time of day on a chart like the one shown in Figure 15 · 4.

Figure 15 · 4.

Date	Time	Temperature in Degrees Centigrade	
		Wheat/Water	Wheat/Formalin

F. Read and record the temperature in each bottle every day for several days. Store the bottles as you did in the previous investigation. If possible, record the temperatures at three-hour intervals during the test. Be sure to lower the thermometer bulb into the center of the mass of wheat grains after each reading.
G. After three or more days, examine some of the grains from each bottle. Describe any differences you may see.

INTERPRETATIONS
1. After observing the differences in the appearance of the grains from the two bottles, do you think formalin affects the germination of wheat grains? If so, describe the effect.
2. Explain any differences in temperature in the two bottles. Why do you suppose formalin affected the temperature as it did?

PROBLEM
1. Suggest other procedures that might add to your understanding of the factors affecting the release of heat by yeast cells.

Production of Carbon Dioxide and Release of Energy

While working with yeast (Investigation 61) you may have noticed that the yeast mixture gave off bubbles. Joseph Priestly (1773–1804), an English clergyman and chemist, noticed the same thing and thought there might be some connection between the bubbles and the life processes of yeast. In his time, all gases were called "air." You might assume that the bubbles could be one of several gases—hydrogen, oxygen, nitrogen, carbon dioxide, or air (which includes oxygen, nitrogen, and carbon dioxide).

Various tests can be used to identify the gas in the bubbles. A glowing splint of wood will burst into flame if it is thrust into a bottle of oxygen. The same glowing splint would cause a mixture of hydrogen and oxygen gas to explode. The fire on the splint will go out completely if the gas is carbon dioxide.

There is a better test for carbon dioxide: When an unknown gas is bubbled through a clear calcium hydroxide solution (lime water), the solution turns cloudy or milky if the gas is CO_2. In this case, carbon dioxide combines chemically with calcium hydroxide to produce a white insoluble salt, calcium carbonate. The equation can be written:

$$CO_2 + Ca(OH)_2 \longrightarrow CaCO_3 + H_2O$$

In Investigation 63 you are asked to test for the presence of CO_2 in a gas that comes from living things.

INVESTIGATION 63: Processes that Produce CO_2

MATERIALS (per team)

Actively growing yeast culture

Bottle with one-hole stopper and delivery tube

Calcium hydroxide solution $Ca(OH)_2$

4 test tubes

2 beakers

Germinating wheat grains

Bottle with 2-hole stopper and delivery tube

Funnel

Watch with second hand
Soda straws
Candle (about 3 inches long)
Wire
Quart jar with lid
Matches

PROCEDURES

A. Pour the active yeast culture into a bottle until it is nearly full. Insert the one-hole stopper and delivery tube. Place the free end of the delivery tube inside a test tube. Support the tube with a small beaker, as shown in Figure 15 · 5. Pour calcium hydroxide solution into the test tube until about 3 cm of the delivery tube is covered. Observe and describe what happens to the clear solution.

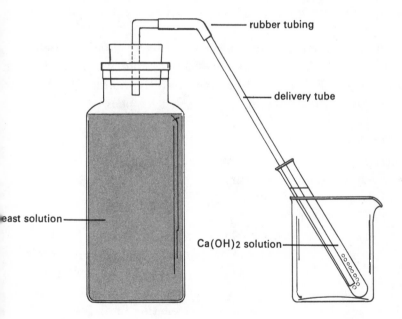

Figure 15 · 5.
Set-up for
Procedure A.

rubber tubing

delivery tube

east solution

Ca(OH)₂ solution

B. Half-fill another bottle with germinating wheat seeds. Insert the two-hole stopper and tubes, as shown in Figure 15 · 6. Allow the apparatus to stand overnight.

Figure 15 · 6.
Set-up for Pro-
cedures B and C.

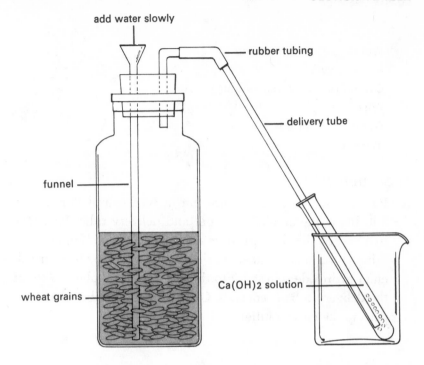

C. On the next day place the end of the delivery tube in a test
tube, and add calcium hydroxide solution. Pour water slowly
into the funnel. This will force gas from the bottle into the
calcium hydroxide solution. Record what happens.

INTERPRETATIONS

1. What is produced by the growing culture of yeast? What is
produced by the germinating wheat grains?

PROCEDURES (continued)

D. Have one member of your team count the number of breaths
he takes per minute while standing quietly. He should breathe
normally and repeat his count several times. Record each trial,
and calculate the average. Have him breathe steadily through
a straw into a test tube of $Ca(OH)_2$ solution until a precipitate forms. Note the time required for the formation of the
precipitate, and record it in your notebook.

E. Have the same member of your team stand up and run in place
for one minute. As soon as he stops, have him blow into a fresh

calcium hydroxide solution, as in Procedure D. Again note and record the time required for a precipitate to form. He should then determine the number of breaths he is taking per minute. Record this number.

INTERPRETATIONS (continued)

2. How did the rate of breathing at rest differ from the rate of breathing after exercise?
3. What influence did exercise have on the amount of carbon dioxide released?
4. You probably noticed that you feel warmer after running or other vigorous exercise than when you remain quiet. Suggest a reason for this difference and for any differences between the results of Procedures D and E.

PROCEDURES (continued)

F. Wrap stiff wire around a candle, as shown in Figure 15·7. Light the candle and lower it into a quart jar. Bend the free end of the wire over the lip of the jar. Let the candle burn for five minutes. Screw the lid on the jar. When the flame goes out, remove the lid and the candle. Pour 25 ml of calcium hydroxide solution into the jar. Replace the lid. Shake the contents gently for one minute and determine whether or not a precipitate forms.

INTERPRETATIONS (continued)

5. In what ways are the reactions observed in Investigations 61 and 62 and in Procedures A, C, E, and F of Investigation 63 similar? In what ways are they different?

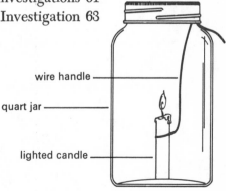

Figure 15·7. Set-up for Procedure F.

wire handle

quart jar

lighted candle

INVESTIGATION 64: Further Study of a Burning Candle

MATERIALS (per team)
  Candle
  Small beaker or jar
  Matches
  Quart jar
  Washcloth
  Pie pan or cake plate

PROCEDURES

A. Light the candle. Hold it horizontally and allow about 5 drops of melted wax to drip onto the center of the pan. Set the candle upright on the wax in the pan.

B. Observe and record the appearance of the candle flame. Using a damp cloth to protect your fingers, hold a small beaker or jar, mouth down, just above the flame. Record your observations.

C. Turn the jar over so that its bottom just touches the top of the flame. Observe the bottom of the jar.

D. Add water to the pan to a depth of 1 cm. Light the candle and lower a jar, mouth down, over the burning candle until it is standing in the pan (Figure 15 · 8). Record your observations.

Figure 15 · 8.
Set-up for
Procedure D.

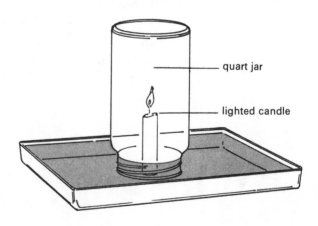

quart jar

lighted candle

INTERPRETATIONS

1. What materials appear to be given off by a burning candle?
2. What happened in the jar during Procedure D? Why?
3. Why didn't the water move into the jar while the candle was burning?
4. Review the results of Procedure F in Investigation 63. Using that information together with what you have gained from this investigation, write a word equation that will describe the reaction of paraffin with a flame.

PROBLEM

1. In Investigations 61-64, energy was released by yeast, wheat, paraffin, and by you.
   a. What substance was produced when energy was released?
   b. What name is usually given to the materials that living things use to produce energy?

REFERENCES

BSCS. *An Inquiry into Life.* New York: Harcourt, Brace & World, 1968.

BSCS. *Green Version: High School Biology.* Chicago: Rand McNally & Co., 1968.

BSCS. *Molecules to Man.* Boston: Houghton Mifflin Co., 1968.

Faraday, Michael. *Chemical History of a Candle.* New York: The Thomas Y. Crowell Co., 1957.

Herz, Werner. *The Shape of Carbon Compounds: An Introduction to Organic Chemistry.* New York: W. A. Benjamin, Inc., 1963.

Molecules Important For Life

Compounds of Carbon

Elements can combine in various ways to produce thousands of different compounds. Salts are formed when metals combine with nonmetals. Other combinations of elements produce acids and bases. Of all the elements known to man, carbon is perhaps the most important for living things. All essential compounds in living matter contain carbon.

Perhaps your model of atomic structure can yield a clue about the importance of carbon to life. Carbon atoms can combine with each other and with atoms of other elements to form thousands of different compounds, including those that make up living matter. You have learned that when most atoms combine with others they tend to gain or lose electrons. The ions produced have electron groupings like those of inert gases. With the exception of helium, atoms of the inert gases have 8 electrons in their outermost regions. (Some kinds of atoms share electrons instead of gaining or losing them. Carbon is an example of an element whose atoms share electrons.)

The atomic number of carbon is 6. A neutral atom of carbon has 6 protons in the nucleus and 6 electrons in the regions surrounding the nucleus—2 electrons in the first region and 4 in the second, or outer, region.

If a carbon atom lost 4 electrons, it would have only 2 electrons remaining. It would then have the same electron arrangement as an atom of helium. On the other hand, if a carbon atom gained 4 electrons, it would have 8 electrons in its outer region. This would be the same as the arrangement found in the inert gas neon. But carbon atoms do not appear to gain or lose electrons when they combine. Instead, they share electrons with other atoms. In this way they have an electron structure like an inert gas without forming ions.

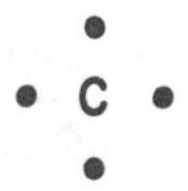

**Figure 16 · 1.
Carbon atom.**

To better understand the structure of carbon compounds, let us examine some simple formulas. For convenience we will concentrate only on the electrons in the outermost region. The carbon atom is represented by the letter C and four dots, one for each of the outer electrons (Figure 16 · 1).

The hydrogen atom is represented by the letter H and one dot for the single electron (Figure 16 · 2).

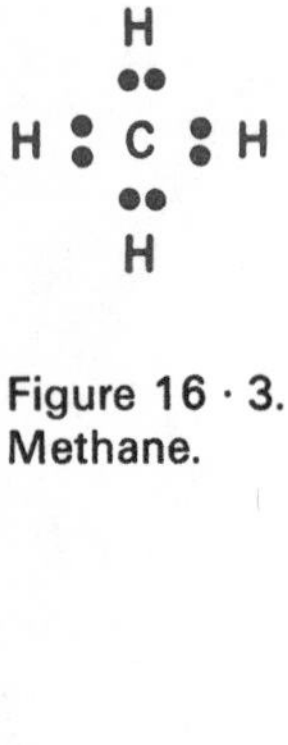

**Figure 16 · 2.
Hydrogen atom.**

Carbon combines readily with hydrogen to form a gas called methane, the chief ingredient of natural gas (Figure 16 · 3).

Notice the arrangement of "electrons" in methane. Because they share electrons with carbon, each hydrogen atom has 2 electrons in its outer region. This is the same electron arrangement as that of the inert gas helium. Similarly, carbon shares the electrons from the four hydrogen atoms and has a total of 8 electrons in its outer region—the same electron arrangement as that of the inert gas neon. You may wish to review the Periodic Table (page 78) to see this more clearly.

**Figure 16 · 3.
Methane.**

The *sharing* of electrons among atoms permits the formation of a greater number of compounds than does ionization—which requires the *transfer* of electrons. Since carbon atoms are able to share electrons with other carbon atoms, they can form a great variety of compounds. In addition to methane, there are many other compounds containing carbon and hydrogen—ethane, for example (Figure 16 · 4).

Ethane, like methane, is found in natural gas. Does each atom in ethane have the electron arrangement of an inert gas?

By means of chemical processes, carbon atoms and hydrogen atoms can be added, forming longer molecules (Figure 16 · 5).

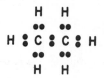

Figure 16 · 4.
Ethane.

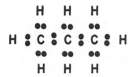

Figure 16 · 5.
Propane.

When 3 carbon and 8 hydrogen atoms are bonded together, they form propane, a "bottle gas" that is often used when natural gas is unavailable.

It would be tedious to go on drawing dots for all the electrons each time we diagram a carbon compound. An internationally accepted system uses dashes between atoms to represent pairs of electrons. The diagrams in Figure 16 · 6 illustrate this convenient method.

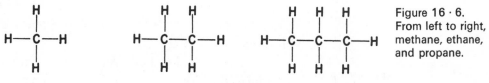

Figure 16 · 6.
From left to right,
methane, ethane,
and propane.

Carbon Compounds in Living Things

Methyl alcohol and paraffin are examples of carbon compounds that burn easily and release energy. Neither is a food. Methyl alcohol is a poison, and no organism (with the possible exception of a few bacteria) can break down the molecules of paraffin. Living organisms also "burn" food and carry on chemical reactions similar to those you have seen in a lighted candle or an alcohol burner. Germinating seeds and active yeast cultures use food and oxygen. In the process, carbon dioxide is liberated and heat energy is given off.

You used molasses as a food for yeast. Sugar is the major ingredient in molasses, and sugar is a nutritious food for many animals. But what is sugar? There are many kinds of sugar, and the names of some of them may be familiar to you: cane sugar, beet sugar, malt sugar, corn sugar, and grape sugar. These names simply indicate the source of the sugar. They tell you nothing about the *structure* of the sugar molecule. Cane and beet sugars are both sucrose, having the formula $C_{12}H_{22}O_{11}$. Corn and grape sugars are glucose, with the formula $C_6H_{12}O_6$.

Fruit sugar is fructose, or levulose. Although its formula, $C_6H_{12}O_6$, is the same as that for glucose, fructose is much sweeter than glucose. But how can two compounds have the same formula and still be different? Formulas such as $C_6H_{12}O_6$ and $C_{12}H_{22}O_{11}$ are called *empirical* formulas. They show the number of different kinds of atoms that make up the molecules. But such formulas do not show how the atoms are arranged in molecules.

Suppose two men have equal quantities of bricks, sand, cement, and water. Could you guess what each man will build with his materials? One might build a sidewalk; the other, a fireplace. Each might use all of the materials and have nothing left over. The amount of materials used to build the sidewalk and the fireplace might be identical. Yet the form and use of the two structures would be very different. In the same way, fructose and glucose are made up of identical sets of atoms. But they have different characteristics because they differ in structure.

So far we have described carbon compounds as if the carbon

atoms were arranged in perfectly straight chains. Better models of a 3-carbon compound and a 6-carbon compound are shown in Figures 16·7 and 16·8.

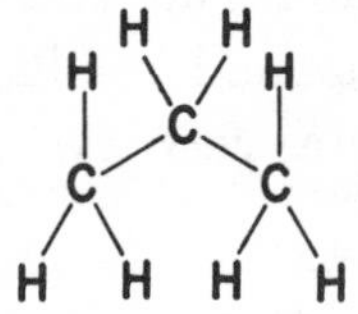

Figure 16·7. Diagram of a propane molecule.

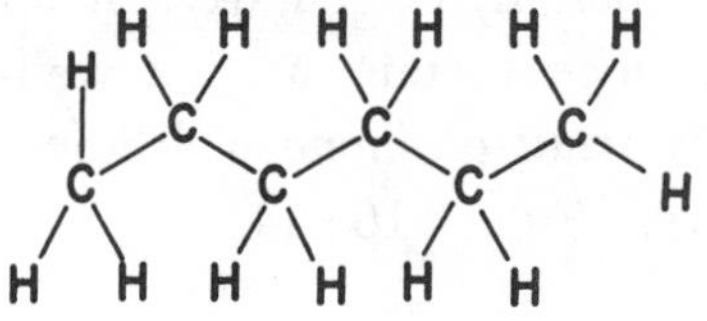

Figure 16·8. Diagram of a hexane molecule.

The zig-zag shape of these molecules is constantly changing. Under certain conditions, each of the end carbons may lose a hydrogen atom and form a ringlike structure, as shown in Figures 16·9 and 16·10.

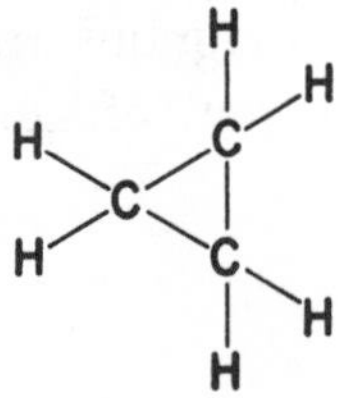

Figure 16·9. Cyclopropane.

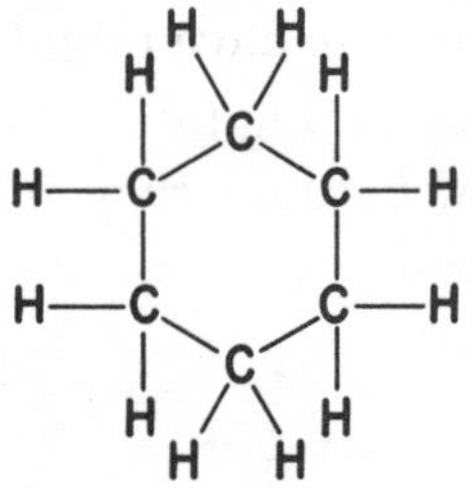

Figure 16·10. Cyclohexane.

A more convenient method of diagraming these two "ringlike" compounds is shown in Figures 16·11 and 16·12. For simplicity the bonds between carbon and hydrogen are not shown.

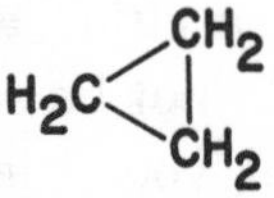

Figure 16·11. Cyclopropane.

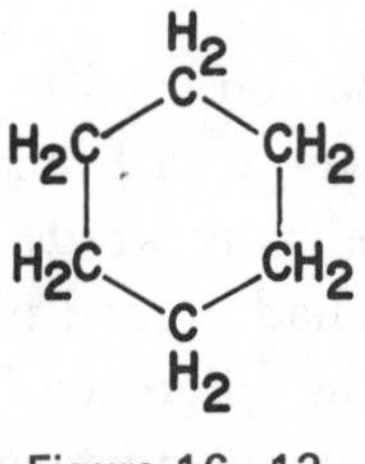

Figure 16·12. Cyclohexane.

Benzene, a ringlike compound somewhat similar to cyclohexane, is illustrated in Figure 16 · 13. Thousands of different drugs, dyes, explosives, and other chemicals are produced from benzene.

If carbon, hydrogen, oxygen, and nitrogen atoms are added to benzene in a certain way, a well-known compound results. Its name is *trinitrotoluene* (abbreviated TNT), a very powerful explosive. (Figure 16 · 14).

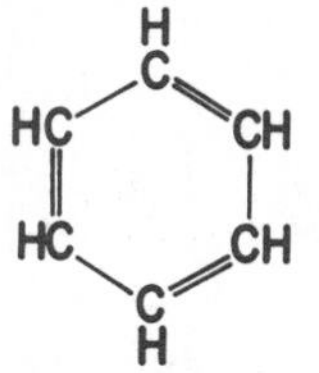

Figure 16 · 13.
Benzene.

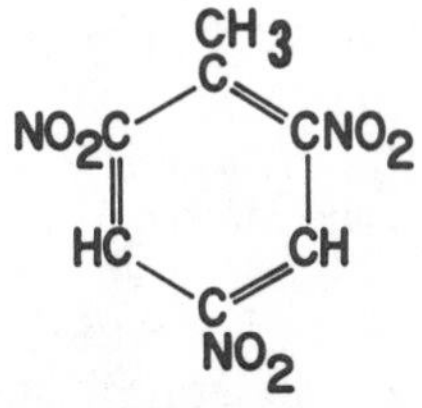

Figure 16 · 14.
Trinitrotoluene.

Sugars also have ringlike structures. Examine and compare the molecules in Figure 16 · 15. We call these diagrams *structural formulas*, because they indicate the arrangement of atoms and their bonds.

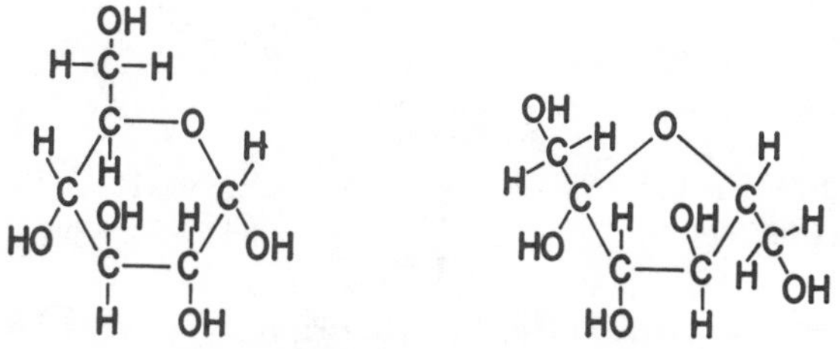

glucose

fructose

Figure 16 · 15. Structural formulas for glucose and fructose.

Suppose you tried to describe the difference between a horse and a donkey to a friend who had never seen either animal. It would take many words. Even then you might not be successful. But if you had a good picture of each animal, your friend could easily see the difference. This does not mean that he would be able to draw accurate pictures of horses and donkeys. But he would have a much better understanding than if he had to rely only on your word description. For a similar reason, many structural formulas of chemical compounds are included in this book. It is not necessary to memorize these formulas. But it *is* important that you examine them carefully and see how they differ. Slight differences in structural formulas can cause great differences in the behavior of chemicals. For example, some bacteria can use glucose as a food, but not fructose. Other bacteria can use fructose, but not glucose. Man can obtain energy from both.

In addition to glucose and fructose, several other sugars have the formula $C_6H_{12}O_6$. Still others, called *simple* sugars, have the formulas $C_5H_{10}O_5$ or $C_7H_{14}O_7$. Some of these are important in the chemistry of living things. Sugars such as maltose and sucrose (table sugar) are formed by joining two simple sugar molecules. Figure 16 · 16 shows how the removal of an OH group and a hydrogen atom from two simple sugar molecules will bond the two together. A molecule of water is given off as a by-product.

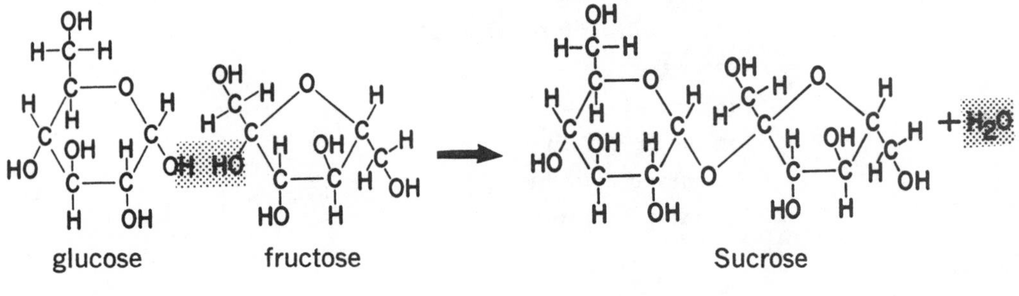

Figure 16 · 16. Formation of sucrose and water from glucose and fructose.

Sucrose is called a *compound* sugar because it is made up of two simple sugars. Other compounds are formed by combining many molecules of simple sugars in long chains. One example is starch; another is cellulose, a basic substance in the walls of plant cells.

INVESTIGATION 65: Some Reactions of Sugars

A chemical indicator called Benedict's solution may be used to detect the presence of certain sugars. To test for these sugars, you add Benedict's solution to a sugar solution and heat the mixture. If the heated solution turns green, orange, or reddish-brown, the presence of sugar is indicated. Not all sugars will react in this manner. During this investigation you will use Benedict's solution as a test for the presence of sugars.

MATERIALS (per team)
   5 test tubes
   5% glucose solution
   5% fructose solution
   5% sucrose solution
   Dilute hydrochloric acid
   Water bath
   Ring stand
   Burner or hot plate
   Graduated cylinder
   Benedict's solution

PROCEDURES

A. Number the test tubes *1* through *5*. Copy Figure 16 · 17 in your notebook.
B. Pour ingredients into each tube as indicated in Figure 16 · 17.
C. Place Tube 5 in a water bath. Heat the water to boiling, and boil gently for five minutes.
D. Add 2 ml of Benedict's solution to each tube.
E. Place all tubes in the water bath, and reheat to boiling. Record your observations.

Figure 16 · 17.

Tube	Contents	Results
1	2 ml of water	
2	2 ml of 5% glucose solution	
3	2 ml of 5% fructose solution	
4	2 ml of 5% sucrose solution	
5	2 ml of 5% sucrose solution + 4 drops dilute HCl	

INTERPRETATIONS

1. What purpose does Tube 1 serve?
2. Compare results from Tubes 4 and 5. How might you explain the difference?
3. If you wanted to test for the presence of sucrose with Benedict's solution, what procedure would you use?

INVESTIGATION 66: Starch and Sugars

A solution of water, iodine, and potassium iodide will turn purple or black in the presence of starch. The use of this indicator (IKI) may help you to gain some information about the relationship between starches and sugars.

MATERIALS (per team)

Clean paraffin or clean rubber bands

Beakers

6 test tubes

Potato or corn starch (3% suspension in water)

5% glucose solution

IKI solution

Benedict's solution

Bunsen burners

Water bath

PROCEDURES

A. Have several members of the class chew small pieces of paraffin or rubber bands to stimulate their salivary glands. As saliva forms, collect it in a glass beaker. Each team will need about 4 ml of saliva.

B. Number the test tubes 1 through 6. Copy Figure 16 · 18 carefully in your notebook, and add information to it as you carry out the procedures.

C. Add 2 ml of glucose solution to Tubes 1 and 2. Shake the starch suspension thoroughly before taking it from the bottle. Add 2 ml of starch suspension to Tubes 3 through 6.

D. Add 2 ml of saliva to Tubes 5 and 6. Allow all tubes to stand for at least twenty minutes. (If there is not time to complete this investigation in one period, the tubes may be left overnight, and the experiment completed the next day.)

E. Add 2 ml of IKI solution to Tubes 2, 4, and 6. Observe the color in each of these tubes.

F. Add 2 ml of Benedict's solution to Tubes 1, 3, and 5. Observe the color in each of these tubes. Heat Tubes 1, 3, and 5 in a water bath. Boil the water in the bath gently for about five minutes. Observe the color in each tube after heating.

Tube	Contents	Treatment	Results
1			
2			
3			
4			
5			
6			

Figure 16 · 18.

INTERPRETATIONS

1. Review the completed chart in your notebook, and explain the results.
2. What appears to be the effect of saliva on starch?
3. What further experiments should be performed to check your hypothesis about the effect of saliva?

Food and Energy

When the bonds that hold atoms together are broken, energy is absorbed. But when atoms combine, energy is *released*. For example, when methyl alcohol burns, heat is released and carbon dioxide and water are formed.

$$2\,CH_3OH \;+\; 3\,O_2 \longrightarrow 2\,CO_2 \;+\; 4\,H_2O \;+\; Energy$$

| methyl alcohol | oxygen | carbon dioxide | water |

In this reaction, energy is used up in breaking the bonds between atoms of alcohol and between atoms of oxygen. On the other hand, energy is released as the carbon-oxygen bonds in CO_2 and the oxygen-hydrogen bonds in H_2O are formed. The total amount of energy released is greater than the total amount of energy used. Most of this energy is released as heat.

When yeast cells use glucose for food, some energy is released as heat. You saw evidence of this in the rise in temperature of a yeast culture in a thermos bottle. A change in the structure of the glucose molecules must have occurred before this energy was released. You saw other evidence that a chemical change was taking place. Carbon dioxide bubbled from the mixture. Under certain conditions the "burning" of glucose can occur in the complete absence of air by a process called *alcoholic fermentation*.

$$C_6H_{12}O_6 \longrightarrow 2\,CO_2 \;+\; C_2H_5OH \;+\; Energy$$

| glucose | carbon dioxide | ethanol (ethyl alcohol) |

Notice that no free oxygen is used, but energy is released. More energy was released in the formation of bonds in carbon dioxide and in ethanol than was required to break the bonds in the glucose molecule. Part of this energy was used by yeast cells, and part of it was released as heat.

Most living cells require oxygen when breaking down molecules in food. And as in the burning of alcohol or paraffin, carbon dioxide and water are formed as heat is given off. The complete burning of glucose in the presence of oxygen can be summarized in the following equation.

$$C_6H_{12}O_6 \;+\; 6\,O_2 \longrightarrow 6\,CO_2 \;+\; 6\,H_2O \;+\; \text{Energy}$$

glucose   oxygen   carbon   water
dioxide

Recall that in Investigation 63, you blew through a straw into calcium hydroxide solution. You then detected the presence of carbon dioxide. In the same investigation, the gas given off by germinating seeds was also identified as carbon dioxide.

Sugars, starches, and cellulose belong to a larger group of compounds called *carbohydrates*. These are important sources of food for most living things.

Another group of compounds containing only carbon, hydrogen, and oxygen are *fats*. In most fats the ratio of hydrogen atoms to oxygen atoms is greater than 2 to 1. That is, there are more than twice as many hydrogen atoms per molecule as there are oxygen atoms. But there are other, more important differences between carbohydrates and fats.

A molecule of fat can be broken down to form two different kinds of substances. One of these substances is glycerol—$C_3H_8O_3$. You will recall that alcohols—such as methyl and ethyl alcohol—are compounds made up of carbon atoms, hydrogen atoms, and OH groups. Glycerol is an alcohol (Figure 16 · 19).

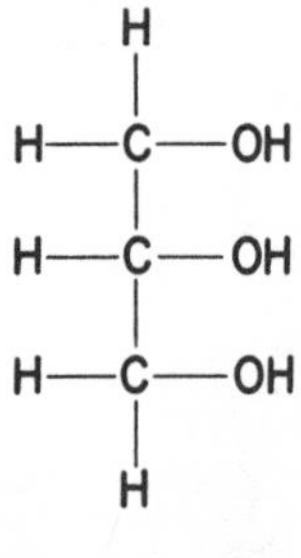

The other substances found when we break apart a fat molecule are called *fatty acids*. There are many kinds of fatty acids. Each one contains a carbon atom to which an OH group and an oxygen atom are bonded.

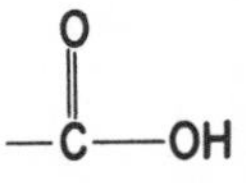

The group shown in Figure 16 · 20 is called an acid group because the hydrogen may be pulled away from the oxygen and become a hydrogen ion (H^+). The simplest acid of this kind is formic acid (Figure 16 · 21). If you have ever squashed an ant between your fingers you may have smelled the formic acid found in these insects.

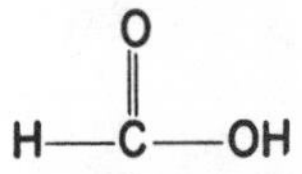

Certain bacteria are able to change ethyl alcohol into vinegar (a dilute solution of acetic acid), as shown in Figure 16 · 22. These bacteria use some of the energy given off during the reaction.

Figure 16 · 19. Glycerol. (Also called glycerine.)

Figure 16 · 20. Acid group.

Figure 16 · 21. Formic acid.

Wine, which contains ethyl alcohol, may turn to vinegar (acetic acid) because of the presence of bacteria.

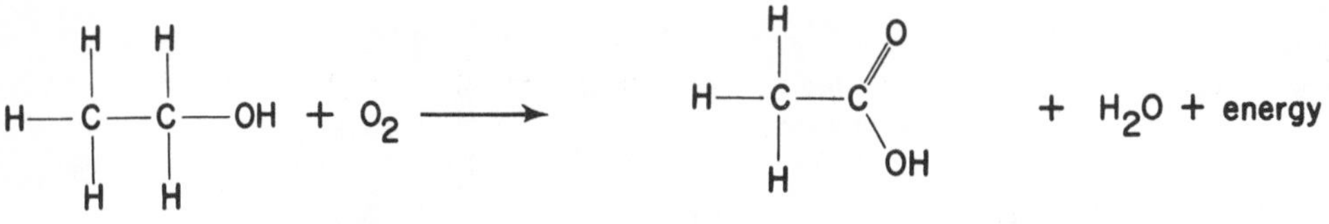

Figure 16 · 22. Formation of acetic acid from ethyl alcohol.

Acids with small molecules (such as those in formic or acetic acid) are not fatty acids, because they are not found in fats. Typical fatty acids contain from 4 to 20 carbon atoms.

A fat molecule is formed by combining 3 fatty acid molecules with one glycerol molecule. In the process 3 water molecules are removed. Because there are so many kinds of fatty acids, and because each fat molecule has 3 fatty acid molecules, a great many kinds of fats are known.

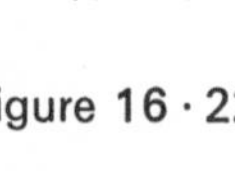

The third major class of foods is made up of *proteins*. Carbohydrates and fats contain only three elements—carbon, hydrogen, and oxygen. Proteins are composed of carbon, hydrogen, oxygen, nitrogen, and sulfur. Fats are made from glycerol and fatty acids, and the more complex carbohydrates are composed of simple sugars joined together. Proteins, too, are made from smaller units. The building blocks of proteins are called *amino acids*. All amino acids contain carbon, hydrogen, oxygen, and nitrogen. A few contain sulfur.

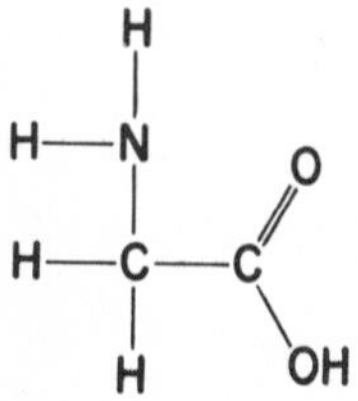

Figure 16 · 23. Amino group.

The amino group is shown in Figure 16 · 23. The simplest amino acid is glycine (Figure 16 · 24). Notice that it contains the same acid group as acetic acid (Figure 16 · 22). In addition, it contains the amino group, which replaces one of the hydrogen atoms in acetic acid.

Figure 16 · 24. Glycine.

Amino acids have an acid group and an amino group. The amino group is attached to the carbon atom next to the acid group. Additional amino groups and additional acid groups may be present, along with other carbon, hydrogen, and oxygen atoms (Figure 16 · 25).

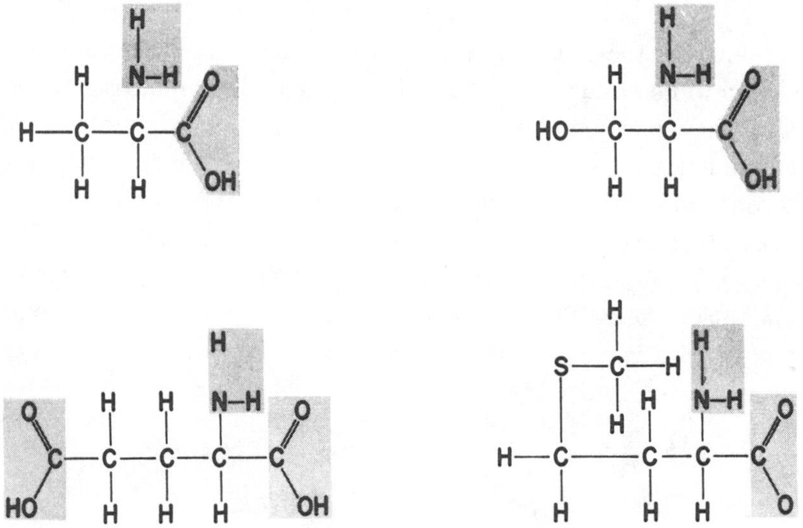

Figure 16 · 25.
Amino acids.

About twenty different amino acids are found in proteins. The amino acids are joined together when one of the hydrogens of the amino group and an OH group from an acid group are removed— in the form of water. This results in the formation of a bond from the nitrogen atom of one amino acid to a carbon atom of another amino acid, as shown in Figure 16 · 26.

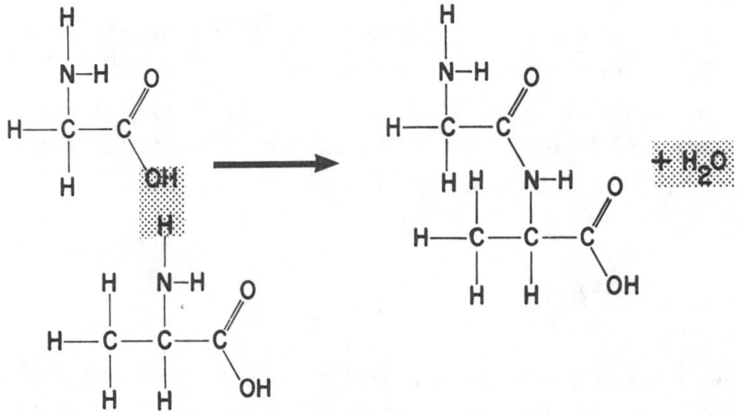

Figure 16 · 26. Formation of a carbon-to-nitrogen bond by removal of a water molecule from two amino acid molecules.

Again, it is not necessary that you memorize these structural formulas or the reactions between molecules. The diagrams are shown to help make clear the differences among amino acids and how they may combine to form proteins. Note that after the amino acids have combined, there is still a free amino group left on one, and a free acid group left on another. These may combine with other amino acid molecules to build up longer and longer chains. A single protein molecule may contain several hundred amino acid units. The combinations possible from twenty different amino acids is almost without limit. Millions of different kinds of proteins are formed.

Energy Requirements of Living Things

Living things use energy for many purposes. The formation of new compounds, the distribution of material within a cell, and the movement of an organism's body—each requires energy. Release of heat energy by chemical reactions in living cells may help cells maintain temperature at levels favorable to their growth and normal activity. Even the transmitting of a stimulus in a nerve cell requires energy. Since thought processes depend on the transmission of messages through many brain cells, thinking requires energy!

Foods are a source of potential energy. This energy is released by chemical reactions in the body. *More energy is released in the formation of the products of these reactions than is absorbed in breaking the bonds of the food molecules.* This surplus energy is available for use in the living cells.

Sources of Foods

Where do organisms obtain food? You may get most of your foods from the garden, the meat market, and the grocery store. But what is the source of food for the cows that produce milk? And what is the source of food for the chickens that produce eggs? If you trace back to the original source of food for most living things, you find it to be green plants.

Parts of green plants have served as food for man since prehistoric times. Cave men probably used seeds and fruits as food. Long before man learned to write, he learned to plant and harvest crops and to save the seeds from one harvest for the next year's planting.

We do not know when man first began to wonder about how plants make food. By the middle of the seventeenth century some experiments had been performed that provided a crude understanding of food production in plants. Between 1775 and 1825 rapid progress was made in explaining how plants make food. Much of this progress was possible because of new discoveries in chemistry.

By 1860 a fairly accurate description of the process of food making in plants was possible. Because this process involved the synthesis (putting together) of foods and because light was required as a source of energy, it was called *photosynthesis*.

One of the great contributors to the study of photosynthesis was the Austrian physician Jan Ingen-Housz. In 1779 Ingen-Housz published a report summarizing 500 separate experiments he had performed during the previous year.

Eugene I. Rabinowitch, in an article on photosynthesis in the *Scientific American* in 1950, wrote, "In photosynthesis, we are like travelers in an unknown country around whom the early morning fog slowly begins to rise, vaguely revealing the outlines of the landscape. It will be thrilling to see it in brigh daylight." He was referring to the fundamental life process by which green plants change simple, inert, inorganic chemicals into the complex, reactive, unstable, energy-rich substances which are the original source of all food. Jan Ingen-Housz was the first to penetrate this unknown country, which to this day has not yet yielded up all its secrets.[1]

A part of the Ingen-Housz report is given on the following pages. Some of the words may be strange, but the writing is typ-

---

[1]*Moments of Discovery*, Vol. II, eds. Bishop and Schwartz (New York: Basic Books, Inc., 1958) p. 612. Used by permission of the publisher.

ical of his time. Read his report carefully, because the work of Ingen-Housz paved the way for much of our modern understanding of how green plants produce sugars, proteins, and other substances vital for life.

JAN INGEN-HOUSZ (1730–1799)

The Process of Photosynthesis in
Green Plants Is Described in
A Series of Experiments

EXPERIMENTS UPON VEGETABLES

I was not long engaged in this enquiry before I saw a most important scene opened to my view: I observed, that plants not only have a faculty to correct bad air in six or ten days, by growing in it, as the experiments of Dr. Priestley indicate, but that they perform this important office in a compleat manner in a few hours; that this wonderful operation is by no means owing to the vegetation of the plant, but to the influence of the light of the sun upon the plant. I found that plants have, moreover, a most surprising faculty of elaborating the air which they contain, and undoubtedly absorb continually from the common atmosphere, into real and fine dephlogisticated air [oxygen]; that they pour down continually, if I may so express myself, a shower of this depurated air, which, diffusing itself through the common mass of the atmosphere, contributes to render it more fit for animal life; that this operation is far from being carried on constantly, but begins only after the sun has for some time made his appearance above the horizon, and has, by his influence, prepared the plants to begin anew their beneficial operation upon the air, and thus upon the animal creation, which was stopt during the darkness of the night; that this operation of the plants is more or less brisk in proportion to the clearness of the day, and the exposition of the plants more or less adapted to receive the direct influence of that great luminary; that plants shaded by high buildings, or growing under a dark shade of other plants, do not perform this office, but, on the contrary, throw out an air hurtful to animals, and even contaminate the air which surrounds them; that this operation of plants diminishes towards the close of the day, and ceases entirely at sun-set, except in a few plants, which continue this duty somewhat longer than others; that this office is not performed by the whole plant, but only by the leaves and the green stalks that support them, that acrid, ill-scented and even the most poisonous plants perform this office in common with the mildness and the most salutary; that the most part of leaves pour out the greatest quantity of this dephlogisticated air from their under surface, principally those of lofty trees; that young leaves, not yet come to their full perfection, yield dephlogisticated air less in quantity, and of an inferior quality, than what is produced by full-grown and old leaves; that some plants elaborate dephlogisticated air better than others; that some of the aquatic plants seem to excell in this operation; that all plants contaminate the surrounding air by night, and even in the day-time in shaded places; that, however, some of those which are inferior to none in yielding beneficial air in the sunshine, surpass others in the power of infecting the circumambient air in the dark even to such a degree, that in a few hours they render a great body of good air so noxious, that an animal placed in it loses its life in a few seconds; that all flowers render the surrounding air highly noxious, equally by night and by day; that the roots removed from the ground do the same, some few however, excepted; but that in general fruits have the same deleterious quality at all times, though principally in the dark, and many to such an astonishing degree, that even some of those fruits which are the most delicious, as, for instance, peaches, contaminate so much the common air as would endanger us to lose our lives, if we were shut up in a room in which a great deal of such fruits are stored up; that the sun by itself has no power to mend air without the concurrence of plants, but on the contrary is apt to contaminate it.

These are some of the secret operations of plants I discovered in my retirement, of which I will endeavour to give some account in the following pages; submitting, however, to the judgement of the candid reader the consequences, which I thought might fairly be deduced from the facts I am to relate . . . .

All plants possess a power of correcting, in a few hours, foul air unfit for respiration; but only in clear daylight, or in the sunshine.

This remarkable property of plants is indeed very great; for in a few hours, nay even sometimes in an hour and a half, they purify so much a body of air quite unfit for respiration, as to be equal in goodness to atmospheric air. They will even do it when they are inclosed in a glass vessel, without any water. One leaf of a vine, shut up in an ounce phial, full of air fouled by breathing so that a candle could not burn in it, restored this air to the goodness of common air in the space of an hour and a half. But plants enjoy this privilege only in the day-time, and when they grow in unshaded places.

This power of plants extends itself even to the worst of all airs, in which an animal finds his destruction in a moment; such as is pure inflamable and highly phlogisticated air, which is little or scarcely at all diminishable by nitrous air. I observed some differences in various kinds of plants in this respect, and found that water plants seem to possess this quality in a greater degree than others. The willow tree and persicaria urens were found eminent in producing this effect; and may it not be providentially ordained it should be so, as those plants grow better in marshy, low grounds, even in stagnated waters, whose bottoms are generally muddy, and yield a great deal of inflammable air, which may be collected at the surface of the water by stirring up the ground, and may be kindled by throwing a burning paper upon the water, which is an amusing experiment by night? Plants, however, want longer time to correct this kind of air, at least that which is extracted from metals by vitriolic acid.

This work is a part of the result of above 500 experiments, all of which were made in less than 3 months, having begun them in June and finished them in the beginning of September, working from morning till night.

SECTION VIII
EXPERIMENTS SHOWING THAT PLANTS HAVE A
REMARKABLE POWER TO CORRECT
BAD AIR IN THE DAY

56.   A sprig of peppermint put in a jar full of air fouled by breathing (so as to extinguish a candle), and exposed to the sun, had corrected this air in three hours so far that a candle could burn in it.

57.   A sprig of nettle was put in a jar full of air fouled by breathing so as to extinguish a candle; it was placed in a room during the whole night; next morning the air was found as bad as before. The jar was put at 9 in the morning in the sunshine; in the space of two hours the air was so much corrected, that it was found to be nearly as good as common air.

SECTION XIX
EXPERIMENTS SHOWING THAT THE SUN BY ITSELF, WITHOUT
THE ASSISTANCE OF PLANTS, DOES NOT IMPROVE AIR,
BUT RENDERS IT RATHER WORSE

124.   Two jars, half full of air taken from the atmosphere at the same time, and half full of pump water, were left by themselves during 4 hours, the one exposed to a bright sunshine, the other placed within the house, only two steps from a door opening in the garden.

The air kept in the house gave, in six different trials, constantly the appearance of being better than that of the jar placed in the sun. One measure of the air kept within doors with one of nitrous air occupied 1.06½ whereas that exposed to the sun occupied 1.02½.

I must acknowledge, however, that this experiment ought to be repeated more than once, to put the fact out of any doubt. I made it the very last day of my stay in the country and thus had not time to repeat it.

Notes on the Work of Ingen-Housz

At the time Ingen-Housz performed his experiments, oxygen, hydrogen, nitrogen, and carbon dioxide were unknown to most scientists. Air was thought to be the only "gas." And it was widely believed that air has many properties: it could be "noxious" (poisonous) or "good" (fit to breathe). Air from stagnant water in marshes would burn. This "inflammable air," which Ingen-Housz found amusing to watch burn, was really methane formed from rotting vegetable material. He refers to marsh air as being the same as the air "extracted from metals by vitriolic acid." Actually the two gases are not the same. If certain metals are placed in sulfuric acid, hydrogen gas is given off. "Vitriolic acid" is an old name for sulfuric acid. Ingen-Housz assumed that the two kinds of "air" were the same, because both burned.

QUESTIONS AND INTERPRETATIONS

1. What was the gas that Ingen-Housz called "bad," "injured," and "noxious" air?
2. What essential experiment led Ingen-Housz to conclude that plants alone cannot restore "injured" air?
3. Though he knew very little about gases and the role of light in photosynthesis, Ingen-Housz made many valuable observations about plants. Review his report, and make a list of the statements you think might be useful in understanding photosynthesis.
4. Do you think Ingen-Housz was correct in his assumption that plants could "restore" air in the absence of water? Explain your answer in terms of the experiment Ingen-Housz described in his report.
5. From his last experiment, Ingen-Housz concluded that the action of sunlight alone could "injure" air. He also stated that he was not sure of his results and that the experiment should be repeated. Suggest a reason why Ingen-Housz might have reached a false conclusion. Design an experiment that would allow you to determine whether or not Ingen-Housz was correct.

6. Why did Ingen-Housz believe that peaches and other fruit "injured" air?

During the next series of investigations you will study some features of photosynthesis that Ingen-Housz could not explore because he lacked certain information and techniques. An important part of science is applying information gathered by others to new experiments.

INVESTIGATION 67: Chlorophyll and Photosynthesis

In Investigation 66 you saw that IKI solution can be used as a test for starch. To obtain a satisfactory starch test in plants, it is necessary to kill the cells of a green leaf and to remove the chlorophyll from the cells before adding the IKI solution.

MATERIALS (per team)
> **Healthy coleus plant with variegated leaves**
> **2 beakers (100-ml)**
> **Water bath**
> **Ring stand**
> **Bunsen burner or hot plate**
> **50 ml alcohol or ditto fluid**
> **IKI solution**
> **1 petri dish (or any flat dish)**

PROCEDURES

A. Sketch a healthy, average-size coleus leaf, showing the color of each area.

B. Place a beaker containing 50 ml of water in a water bath. The water in the bath should be about 1 inch deep.

C. Place the water bath on a ring stand over a Bunsen burner or on a hot plate, and bring the water to a boil.

D. Remove a leaf from the plant and immerse it in the boiling water in the beaker for about one minute. Remove the beaker from the hot water bath (but keep the bath hot). Observe and record any color changes in the leaf.

E. Turn off the Bunsen burner (or hot plate). Immediately place a beaker containing 50 ml of alcohol in the hot water bath.

CAUTION: *Alcohol is flammable. Do not place a container of alcohol directly over an open flame. Heating the alcohol inside a water bath is relatively safe.*

F. Carefully immerse the boiled leaf in the hot alcohol. Do not remove the leaf from the alcohol until the leaf has lost most of the green color.

G. Carefully spread the leaf out on a dish. Note any change of color. Observe and record the appearance of the alcohol in the beaker.

H. Pour a little IKI solution over the entire leaf. Sketch the leaf again, indicating the color of each area.

INTERPRETATIONS

1. Compare the solubility of the pink pigment in water with that of the green chlorophyll in water.

2. Compare the solubility of chlorophyll in water with that of chlorophyll in alcohol.

3. Which areas of the leaf gave a positive test for starch? What seems necessary for starch production in a leaf?

4. If starch is produced only in certain areas, how is the total plant nourished?

INVESTIGATION 68: Light and Food Production

67 provided evidence of some relationship between and the presence of starch in the coleus leaf. A similar may give us some information about a possible relaetween light and food production in a leaf.

ALS (per team)

ᴊssors

ᴊlack paper or aluminum foil

ᴊeranium plant or young bean plant (about 2 weeks old)

Tape or paper clips

200-watt lamp

Beakers

Burner or hot plate

Water bath

Alcohol (ditto fluid)

Flat dish

IKI solution

PROCEDURES

A. Cut a piece of black paper or aluminum foil large enough to cover the middle third of one of the large leaves of the plant,

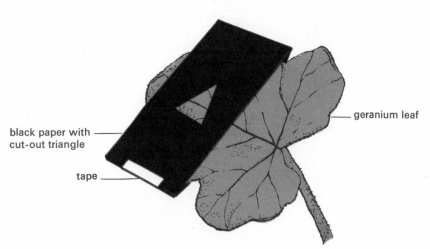

black paper with cut-out triangle

tape

geranium leaf

Figure 16 · 27.
Set-up for
Procedures A–C.

as shown in Figure 16·27. (Do not remove any leaves fr
the plant.) Cut a small design, such as a triangle, in the p
of the paper that will cover the leaf. Fasten the paper in pla
with tape or paper clips.

B. Set a 200-watt lamp about 30 inches above the leaves of th
plant. If necessary, support the covered leaf so that its uppe
surface faces the light source. Water the plant well, and leav
it until the next day.

C. On the following day clip the covered leaf from the plant, and
carefully remove the paper. Immerse the leaf, first in boiling
water, then in hot alcohol, as in Investigation 67. Test for the
presence of starch with IKI solution.

INTERPRETATIONS

1. Was there any difference in the amount of starch present in the
covered and uncovered areas of the leaf?

2. What do the results of this investigation indicate about the
relationship of light and food synthesis in leaves?

3. What do you suppose was the source of energy that appeared
as heat in the yeast culture and germinating seeds in Investigations 61 and 62?

INVESTIGATION 69: Experiments with Leaves Kept in Darkness

From Investigation 68 you may have concluded light is necessary for the production of starch in green leaves. During this investigation you will attempt to verify (support) your conclusion by working with leaves that are not exposed to the light.

MATERIALS (per team)

    6 beakers

    Scissors

    Healthy, variegated-leaved coleus plant which has been left in darkness for 48–72 hours

    Tape

    5% sucrose solution

    Light-tight cardboard box

    Water bath

    Alcohol

    Petri dishes

    IKI solution

PROCEDURES

A. Fill one of the beakers with water, and label it *water*. Cut one of the leaves, with the *petiole* attached (see Figure 16 · 28) from a coleus plant. Place the cut end of the petiole in the water, and lay the blade of the leaf on an inverted jar or beaker, as shown. Repeat with a second leaf, using another jar or beaker to support its blade. Tape the tip of each leaf to the support.

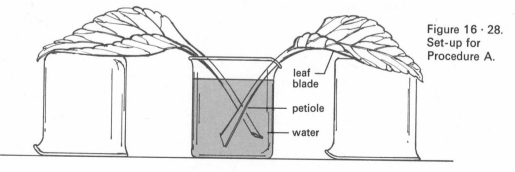

leaf
blade

petiole

water

Figure 16 · 28.
Set-up for
Procedure A.

B. Fill another beaker with 5% sucrose solution, and label it *sucrose*. Remove two more leaves from the plant, and place their petioles in the sugar solution. Place the blades of these leaves on supports. Cover all beakers and leaves with the light-tight box.

C. After 24 to 48 hours, place the two leaves used in Procedure A in boiling water. Remove the pigments, and test for starch as you did in Investigation 67. Repeat the process with the leaves used in Procedure B.

D. Observe each leaf carefully. Make notes and sketches indicating any areas of starch production.

INTERPRETATIONS

1. Is light necessary for the production of starch in coleus leaves? Explain your answer in terms of the results of this investigation.

2. How can you explain the results of this investigation as compared to the results of Investigation 68?

REFERENCES

Asimov, Isaac. *Building Blocks of the Universe.* New York: Abelard-Schuman, Limited, 1961.

Blackwood, Paul E. *Push and Pull: The Story of Energy.* New York: McGraw-Hill Book Co. (Whittlesey House), 1959.

Branley, Franklyn M. *Solar Energy.* New York: The Thomas Y. Crowell Co., 1957.

BSCS. *An Inquiry into Life.* New York: Harcourt, Brace & World, 1968.

BSCS. *Green Version: High School Biology.* Chicago: Rand McNally & Co., 1963.

BSCS. *Molecules to Man.* Boston: Houghton Mifflin Co., 1963.

Galston, Arthur W. *Life of the Green Plant.* Englewood Cliffs, N.J.: Prentice-Hall, 1961.

Hart, Harold, and Schuetz, R. D. *A Short Course in Organic Chemistry.* Boston: Houghton Mifflin Co., 1959.

Particle Size and Energy

Results of the last several investigations indicate that green plants are able to make food in the presence of carbon dioxide, water and sunlight. This process is summarized in the following equation:

$$6\,CO_2 \;+\; 6\,H_2O \xrightarrow[\text{Chlorophyll}]{\text{Light Energy}} C_6H_{12}O_6 \;+\; 6\,O_2$$

$6\,CO_2$ — carbon dioxide $6\,H_2O$ — water $C_6H_{12}O_6$ — sugar $6\,O_2$ — oxygen

The equation for photosynthesis indicates only the final result of a complicated series of chemical reactions—reactions so complex that the process of photosynthesis is still a subject of detailed study.

Photosynthesis occurs in two major steps. The first step is called the *light reaction*, and the second, the *dark reaction*. These terms were suggested following the discovery that light was required for only one phase of photosynthesis—the "splitting" of water molecules. This process is not as simple as it may sound. We can shine light on water indefinitely without causing water molecules to break apart. But in the presence of chlorophyll, light energy can cause the hydrogen-oxygen bonds to break. In the process, energy from light is "captured." This is the light reaction phase of photosynthesis.

Oxygen and hydrogen atoms from the water molecules combine with carbon atoms from carbon dioxide to form energy-rich carbohydrates and fats. This second phase of photosynthesis is called the dark reaction, because it proceeds whether light is present or not. In the complete process (both light and dark reactions) several special compounds store and then transfer the energy—that originally came from light—to food products.

In addition to carbohydrates and fats, plant cells are able to produce proteins. From the soil plants obtain nitrogen, sulfur, phosphorus, and other elements required for protein synthesis. Plants use the food they produce for reproduction, growth, and development. The process of obtaining energy from food is called *respiration* and is summarized in the following equation:

$$C_6H_{12}O_6 \quad + \quad 6\,O_2 \longrightarrow 6\,CO_2 \quad + \quad 6\,H_2O \quad + \quad \text{Energy}$$

sugar   oxygen   carbon   water
                                        dioxide

The amount of energy *released* during the formation of carbon dioxide and water is greater than the amount of energy required to break the bonds between the atoms of the sugar molecule. This released energy is used by plants and animals to sustain life. Recall the results of earlier investigations—in which carbon dioxide was given off by germinating wheat seeds, by a growing yeast culture, and by you (or one of your classmates). The process of respiration occurs in nearly every living thing.

There are other problems that living things must solve if they are to remain alive—problems that involve energy. How does a green plant obtain the carbon dioxide and water it uses in photosynthesis? How does it get rid of the oxygen? How is sugar moved from where it is produced (in the leaf) to where it is stored as starch (in the roots)? How do food and oxygen, which are needed in every living cell, get into those cells? How do cells get rid of waste materials, such as carbon dioxide?

Many questions about the movement of materials in living things will not be answered in this book. Some of the answers are as yet unknown. But we can attempt to answer a few of these questions.

INVESTIGATION 70: The Action of Membranes

Each cell of a living plant or animal is surrounded by a very thin *membrane* through which materials must enter and leave. An artificial cell membrane can be constructed with dialysis tubing. Investigating the behavior of an artificial membrane may provide a model that will help explain the action of membranes surrounding living cells.

MATERIALS (per team)
    2 pint jars or beakers
    100 ml of a starch suspension
    100 ml of dilute IKI solution
    2 pieces of 6-inch dialysis tubing
    Paper clips or rubber bands

PROCEDURES
A. Label the jars *1* and *2*.
B. In Jar 1 prepare a starch suspension by adding starch to water until the mixture becomes cloudy in appearance.
C. Add 100 ml of dilute IKI solution to Jar 2.
D. Tie a knot in one end of each piece of tubing. Fill one tube with starch suspension from Jar 1; fill the other tube with IKI solution from Jar 2. Twist the open end of each tube. Fold it over and fasten it with a paper clip or rubber band.
E. Place the tube with IKI solution in Jar 1 (starch) and the tube with starch in Jar 2 (IKI) as shown in Figure 17 · 1.

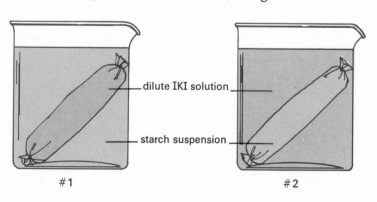

dilute IKI solution

starch suspension

#1   #2

Figure 17 · 1.
Set-up for Procedures E and F.

F. Both jars should be left undisturbed for fifteen minutes. Observe and record what occurs in each jar.

INTERPRETATIONS

1. Describe and explain any changes that may have occurred in the jars.
2. Which substances appear to move through the membrane? Relate your answer to the size of particles involved.
3. Assume that plant cell membranes and the artificial membranes act in the same way. Which substances would be likely to enter or leave a cell more quickly—glucose or starch?

INVESTIGATION 71: Movement of Molecules Against Gravity

Investigation 70 may have given you evidence showing how some molecules are able to pass through membranes while others are not. Investigation 71 will help you understand one of the processes in which water can move into a living plant—even against gravitational force.

MATERIALS (per team)
>   Dialysis tubing
>   Scissors
>   Concentrated sugar solution (Karo syrup)
>   Glass tubing (30 cm)
>   One-hole stopper, to fit end of dialysis tubing
>   String or wire
>   Large jar or beaker
>   Meterstick
>   Ring stand and clamp

PROCEDURES

A. Cut off a piece of dialysis tubing about 5 inches long. Wet the tubing to make it flexible, and tie a knot in one end. Fill the tubing with sugar solution to within one inch of the open end. Insert the stopper and the glass tube. Push the stopper in far enough so the sugar solution rises in the tube to a level just above the top of the stopper. Tie the tubing tightly against the stopper with string or wire.

B. Carefully rinse the outside of the dialysis tubing with water.

C. Place the dialysis tubing in a jar of water.

D. Attach a ruler or meterstick to the glass tube with string or rubber bands. Support (with a ring stand) the ruler and the attached tube in a vertical position. Adjust the apparatus so that the bottom of the dialysis tubing is not resting on the bottom of the jar (see Figure 17 · 2).

E. Measure and record the level of the solution in the glass tube. Repeat this measurement at regular intervals during the class period. Record your measurements.

Figure 17 · 2. Completed set-up for Procedures A–E. The detailed enlargement on the right shows the correct procedure for connecting the dialysis tubing, stopper, and glass tubing.

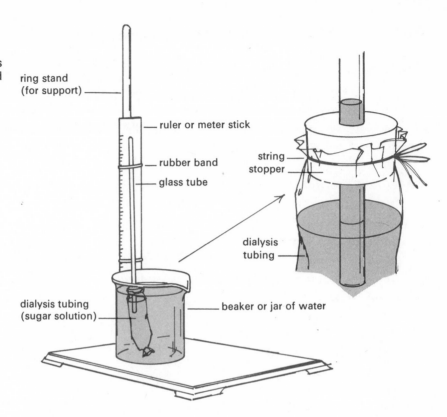

ring stand (for support)

ruler or meter stick

rubber band

glass tube

string

stopper

dialysis tubing

dialysis tubing (sugar solution)

beaker or jar of water

INTERPRETATIONS

1. Predict where the level of the solution will be at the end of one hour and at the end of two hours.
2. Where does the extra liquid come from?
3. Why did the liquid move as it did?
4. Did some of the sugar from inside the membrane move into the water in the jar?
5. What would happen if you added a lot of sugar to the water in the jar?

Diffusion—The Movement of Particles

Diffusion may explain much of the movement of materials into and out of living cells. A leaf uses up carbon dioxide during photosynthesis. The concentration of carbon dioxide inside the leaf cell becomes less than its concentration outside the cell. More carbon dioxide will then diffuse into the leaf from the air outside. This will continue as long as the leaf is using carbon dioxide more rapidly than it is releasing it. But when photosynthesis slows down —as it does at night, for example—the leaf will release more carbon dioxide by respiration than it will take in.

Since oxygen is consumed in respiration and released in photosynthesis, it is likely to diffuse into the leaf at the time carbon dioxide is diffusing out. For in darkness, the leaf cannot photosynthesize. Respiration, on the other hand, never ceases in living cells. When the leaf is exposed to light, photosynthesis is likely to take place more rapidly than respiration. Then carbon dioxide will diffuse in, while oxygen will diffuse out.

Other substances also diffuse from one place to another in living things. Water, sugar, amino acids, and many other compounds may diffuse from cell to cell. You should keep several facts in mind when studying the movement of substances by diffusion. First, diffusion is a relatively slow process. Second, the rate of diffusion depends on the size of the molecules involved. Third, if substances are to diffuse into or out of a cell, they must be able to pass through the membranes surrounding that cell.

You have seen that molecules of IKI, water, and glucose are able to diffuse through a membrane (dialysis tubing). But the movement of glucose through that membrane was very slow, and no movement of starch through the membrane could be detected.

The membranes of living cells are highly complex structures. Under some conditions these membranes may permit the passage of some large molecules and hold back much smaller ones. And the passage of one kind of a molecule may be permitted at one time but prevented at another time. Why membranes behave in this way is not well understood.

Few living things depend entirely on diffusion for the movement of foods and waste materials within them. Higher animals, such as man, have a fluid-transport system that carries both food and waste materials to and from most parts of the body. Your heart serves as the pump that moves your blood around and around through various tissues. But even in higher animals, blood does not *flow* into and out of the cells of the body. The movement of food and oxygen from the blood into the cells takes place largely by means of diffusion. Diffusion also explains most of the movement of such waste materials as CO_2 from the cells into the blood and from the blood into the air sacs in our lungs.

REFERENCES

BSCS. *An Inquiry into Life.* New York: Harcourt, Brace & World, 1968.

BSCS. *Molecules to Man.* Boston: Houghton Mifflin Co., 1968.

Review and a New Beginning

Whether you continue to study in science or not, you have in this course *experienced* the process of science—rather than having just read about it or listened to someone else tell you what it is. You have also experienced some of the satisfactions and frustrations that result from investigating the unknown. And you have seen that success in an investigation usually leads to more new questions than you faced at the start.

You have touched upon some of the knowledge man now possesses about chemistry and physics and the relationships of these subjects to the study of life. Investigative science and the building of scientific models have been emphasized.

If you are planning to take additional science courses in high school or college, we hope that *Interaction of Matter and Energy* has prepared you for the challenges ahead. Keep in mind that no one who undertakes a serious scientific study ever reaches a final plateau of absolute knowledge. It has been estimated that the accumulation of scientific knowledge increases five-fold with each generation. Thousands of men and women are now at work in all areas of science, and some of their discoveries will change what we now accept as scientific "truth."

In Section One we said that there is no sharp dividing line between science and technology and that all branches of science are related. In December, 1967, a team of scientists announced that they had produced a synthetic virus DNA molecule which reproduces itself! Each of the scientists is from a different university, and each has a different background. Their discovery is so significant that many are asking, "Has life been created in a test tube?"

As you may know, DNA (deoxyribonucleic acid) is considered to be the material that makes up genes. Genes, in turn, appear to control inherited characteristics in all living things. The smallest organism that is capable of reproducing itself—a virus—is thought to be composed mostly of DNA.

Viruses cause many diseases, including measles and polio. To reproduce, viruses must enter a living cell and use molecules of the cell DNA to make new virus DNA molecules. That genes and viruses are both made of DNA has interested scientists for many years. The work of Drs. Mehran Goulian, Arthur Kornberg, and Robert Sinsheimer may open the door to many new and exciting discoveries. Scientists are wondering if someday man may be able to use synthetic DNA to cure cancer or to change unwanted, inherited characteristics.

California Institute of Technology

Figure 18 · 1. Electron micrograph of double viral DNA rings synthesized in the test tube at Stanford University School of Medicine. Actual length across is 2 microns (one micron is equal to one millionth of a meter).

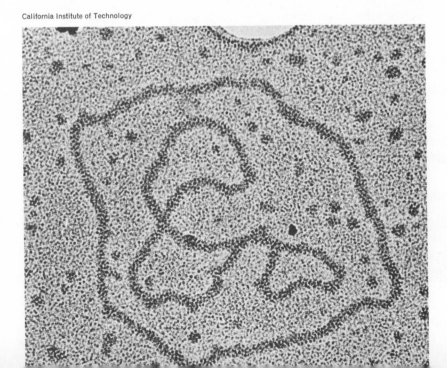

Edgar W. D. Holcomb, San Francisco

California Institute of Technology

Figure 18 · 3. Dr. Robert S. Sinsheimer. Professor of Biophysics at the California Institute of Technology.

Figure 18 · 2. Dr. Arthur Kornberg. Professor of Biochemistry and head of the Department of Biochemistry, Stanford University School of Medicine.

University of Chicago

Figure 18 · 4. Mehran Goulian, M.D. Associate Professor of Medicine at the University of Chicago, School of Medicine.

There has not been time in this course to investigate many of the interesting problems about life. Questions have been raised only to be left unanswered. For example, the process of respiration has been mentioned, but not discussed in detail. We have briefly traced the path of energy from light to glucose. Yet over thirty different chemical reactions occur within the cell of an organism as it breaks down molecules of glucose and releases energy and carbon dioxide. If you enroll in a biology course, you could learn much more about the chemistry of living things.

Interactions of matter and energy continue around you and within you. As a result, all living things, the world, and the universe change from day to day. Rewarding experiences await those who select science as a career. Let us hope that the natural and physical world never looks the same to you again. You now have much more knowledge which should enable you to uncover deeper insights and deeper appreciation of the physical world.

The problems challenging man will increase in number and become more complex in the foreseeable future. We have the power to change our surroundings for better or worse. And we must take care to know, as much as possible, how and when to use our power —or not to use it. *Everyone* has a stake in this.

You need not take additional courses in science to benefit from what science has to offer. When this school year has ended, your investigation of natural and physical surroundings should continue.

Perhaps you will take other courses in science. Even if you do not, you may learn a great deal by observing your surroundings. Education is a life-long process. Persons who can make accurate observations and interpretations are highly valued not only in the sciences, but in all fields of human activity. You have practiced these skills in science. Try to apply them in everything you do.

REFERENCES

Bronowski, Jacob. *The Common Sense of Science.* Cambridge, Mass.: Harvard University Press, 1953.

————. *Science and Human Values.* New York: Harper and Row, 1958.

Dampier, Sir William Cecil. *A History of Science.* 4th ed. London: Cambridge University Press, 1949.

Fox, Russell. *The Science of Science.* New York: Walker & Co., 1963.

Toulmin, Stephen. *Philosophy of Science.* New York: Harper and Row, 1960.

Appendices

Appendix A

COMPLETE PERIODIC TABLE OF THE ELEMENTS

Config	At. wt	Symbol	Z	Name
1	1.0	H	1	HYDROGEN
2,1	6.9	Li	3	LITHIUM
2,2	9.0	Be	4	BERYLLIUM
2,8,1	23.0	Na	11	SODIUM
2,8,2	24.3	Mg	12	MAGNESIUM
2,8,8,1	39.1	K	19	POTASSIUM
2,8,8,2	40.1	Ca	20	CALCIUM
2,8,9,2	45.0	Sc	21	SCANDIUM
2,8,10,2	47.9	Ti	22	TITANIUM
2,8,11,2	51.0	V	23	VANADIUM
2,8,13,1	52.0	Cr	24	CHROMIUM
2,8,13,2	54.9	Mn	25	MANGANESE
2,8,14,2	55.8	Fe	26	IRON
2,8,15,2	58.9	Co	27	COBALT
2,8,18,8,1	85.5	Rb	37	RUBIDIUM
2,8,18,8,2	87.6	Sr	38	STRONTIUM
2,8,18,9,2	88.9	Y	39	YTTRIUM
2,8,18,10,2	91.2	Zr	40	ZIRCONIUM
2,8,18,12,1	92.9	Nb	41	NIOBIUM
2,8,18,13,1	96.0	Mo	42	MOLYBDENUM
2,8,18,13,2	98.9	Tc	43	TECHNETIUM
2,8,18,15,1	101.1	Ru	44	RUTHENIUM
2,8,18,16,1	102.9	Rh	45	RHODIUM
2,8,18,18,8,1	132.9	Cs	55	CESIUM
2,8,18,18,8,2	137.4	Ba	56	BARIUM
2,8,18,18,9,2	138.9	La	57	LANTHANUM
2,8,18,32,10,2	178.5	Hf	72	HAFNIUM
2,8,18,32,11,2	181.0	Ta	73	TANTALUM
2,8,18,32,12,2	183.9	W	74	TUNGSTEN
2,8,18,32,13,2	186.2	Re	75	RHENIUM
2,8,18,32,14,2	190.2	Os	76	OSMIUM
2,8,18,32,15,2	192.2	Ir	77	IRIDIUM
2,8,18,32,18,8,1	(223)	Fr	87	FRANCIUM
2,8,18,32,18,8,2	(226)	Ra	88	RADIUM
2,8,18,32,18,9,2	(227)	Ac	89	ACTINIUM

Lanthanide series:

Config	At. wt	Symbol	Z	Name
2,8,18,20,8,2	139	Ce	58	CERIUM
2,8,18,21,8,2	141	Pr	59	PRASEODYMIUM
2,8,18,22,8,2	144	Nd	60	NEODYMIUM
2,8,18,23,8,2	(147)	Pm	61	PROMETHIUM
2,8,18,24,8,2	150	Sm	62	SAMARIUM
2,8,18,25,8,2	152	Eu	63	EUROPIUM
2,8,18,25,9,2	157	Gd	64	GADOLINIUM
2,8,18,27,8,2	159	Tb	65	TERBIUM
2,8,18,28,8,2	162	Dy	66	DYSPROSIUM

Actinide series:

Config	At. wt	Symbol	Z	Name
2,8,18,32,18,10,2	232	Th	90	THORIUM
2,8,18,32,20,9,2	(231)	Pa	91	PROTACTINIUM
2,8,18,32,21,9,2	238	U	92	URANIUM
2,8,18,32,22,9,2	(237)	Np	93	NEPTUNIUM
2,8,18,32,24,8,2	(239)	Pu	94	PLUTONIUM
2,8,18,32,25,8,2	(241)	Am	95	AMERICIUM
2,8,18,32,25,9,2	(244)	Cm	96	CURIUM
2,8,18,32,26,9,2	(249)	Bk	97	BERKELIUM
2,8,18,32,28,8,2	(249)	Cf	98	CALIFORNIUM

Config	At. Wt.	Symbol	At. No.	Name
2	4.0	He	2	HELIUM

Config	At. Wt.	Symbol	At. No.	Name
2, 3	10.8	B	5	BORON
2, 4	12.0	C	6	CARBON
2, 5	14.0	N	7	NITROGEN
2, 6	16.0	O	8	OXYGEN
2, 7	19.0	F	9	FLUORINE
2, 8	20.2	Ne	10	NEON

Config	At. Wt.	Symbol	At. No.	Name
2, 8, 3	27.0	Al	13	ALUMINUM
2, 8, 4	28.1	Si	14	SILICON
2, 8, 5	31.0	P	15	PHOSPHOROUS
2, 8, 6	32.1	S	16	SULFUR
2, 8, 7	35.5	Cl	17	CHLORINE
2, 8, 8	39.9	Ar	18	ARGON

Config	At. Wt.	Symbol	At. No.	Name
2, 8, 16, 2	58.7	Ni	28	NICKEL
2, 8, 18, 1	63.5	Cu	29	COPPER
2, 8, 18, 2	65.4	Zn	30	ZINC
2, 8, 18, 3	69.7	Ga	31	GALLIUM
2, 8, 18, 4	72.6	Ge	32	GERMANIUM
2, 8, 18, 5	74.9	As	33	ARSENIC
2, 8, 18, 6	79.0	Se	34	SELENIUM
2, 8, 18, 7	79.9	Br	35	BROMINE
2, 8, 18, 8	83.8	Kr	36	KRYPTON

Config	At. Wt.	Symbol	At. No.	Name
2, 8, 18, 18	106.4	Pd	46	PALLADIUM
2, 8, 18, 18, 1	107.9	Ag	47	SILVER
2, 8, 18, 18, 2	112.4	Cd	48	CADMIUM
2, 8, 18, 18, 3	114.8	In	49	INDIUM
2, 8, 18, 18, 4	118.7	Sn	50	TIN
2, 8, 18, 18, 5	121.8	Sb	51	ANTIMONY
2, 8, 18, 18, 6	127.6	Te	52	TELLURIUM
2, 8, 18, 18, 7	126.9	I	53	IODINE
2, 8, 18, 18, 8	131.3	Xe	54	XENON

Config	At. Wt.	Symbol	At. No.	Name
2, 8, 18, 32, 17, 1	195.1	Pt	78	PLATINUM
2, 8, 18, 32, 18, 1	197.0	Au	79	GOLD
2, 8, 18, 32, 18, 2	200.6	Hg	80	MERCURY
2, 8, 18, 32, 18, 3	204.4	Tl	81	THALLIUM
2, 8, 18, 32, 18, 4	207.2	Pb	82	LEAD
2, 8, 18, 32, 18, 5	209.0	Bi	83	BISMUTH
2, 8, 18, 32, 18, 6	(209)	Po	84	POLONIUM
2, 8, 18, 32, 18, 7	(210)	At	85	ASTATINE
2, 8, 18, 32, 18, 8	(222)	Rn	86	RADON

Config	At. Wt.	Symbol	At. No.	Name
2, 8, 18, 29, 8, 2	165	Ho	67	HOLMIUM
2, 8, 18, 30, 8, 2	167	Er	68	ERBIUM
2, 8, 18, 31, 8, 2	169	Tm	69	THULIUM
2, 8, 18, 32, 8, 2	173	Yb	70	YTTERBIUM
2, 8, 18, 32, 9, 2	175	Lu	71	LUTETIUM

Config	At. Wt.	Symbol	At. No.	Name
2, 8, 18, 32, 29, 8, 2	(254)	Es	99	EINSTEINIUM
2, 8, 18, 32, 30, 8, 2	(253)	Fm	100	FERMIUM
2, 8, 18, 32, 31, 8, 2	(256)	Md	101	MENDELEVIUM
2, 8, 18, 32, 32, 8, 2	(254)	No	102	NOBELIUM
2, 8, 18, 32, 32, 9, 2	(257)	Lw	103	LAWRENCIUM

Appendix B

Below are the names of a few scientists and their fields of interest.

1. Aristotle (384–322 B.C.)
Chemistry and Physics
2. Archimedes (287–212 B.C.)
Mathematics and Physics
3. Lucretius (c. 99–55 B.C.)
Chemistry
4. Roger Bacon (c. 1220–1292)
Physics
5. Galileo Galilei (1564–1642)
Physics
6. Blaise Pascal (1623–1662)
Mathematics and Physics
(fluids)
7. Christian Huygens (1629–1693)
Physics (light)
8. Sir Isaac Newton (1642–1727)
Physics (laws of motion)
9. Alessandro Volta (1745–1827)
Physics (electricity)
10. John Dalton (1766–1844)
Chemistry (atomic theory)
11. Amedeo Avogadro (1776–1856)
Chemistry (atomic theory)
12. Jöns Jakob Berzelius (1779–1848)
Chemistry
13. Michael Faraday (1791–1867)
Chemistry (electricity and physics)
14. Sir Joseph John Thomson (1856–1940)
Physics (atomic theory)
15. Svanté August Arrhenius (1859–1927)
Chemistry
16. Ernest Rutherford (1871–1937)
Physics (atomic theory)
17. G. N. Lewis (1875–1946)
Chemistry
18. Linus Pauling (b. 1901——)
Chemistry

Appendix C

CONVERSION TABLES: UNITS OF MEASUREMENTS

LENGTH

English to Metric
1 mile = 1.6094 kilometers
1 yard = 0.9144 meter
1 foot = 0.3048 meter
1 inch = 2.5400 centimeters

Metric to English
1 kilometer = 0.6214 mile
1 meter = 1.0936 yards
1 centimeter = 0.3937 inch
1 millimeter = 0.03937 inch

Metric to Metric
1 kilometer = 1000 meters
1 meter = 100 centimeters
1 centimeter = 10 millimeters
1 meter = 1 million microns
1 meter = 1000 millimeters
1 micron = 1000 millimicrons

VOLUME

English to Metric
1 gallon = 3.7853 liters
1 quart = 0.9463 liter
1 pint = 0.4731 liter
1 ounce = 29.6 milliliters
(fluid)
1 cubic = 16.3868 milliliters
inch

Metric to English
1 liter = 1.0567 quarts
1 milliliter = 0.0338 ounce
(fluid)
1 cubic centi- = 0.0338 ounce
meter (fluid)

Equivalents
1 liter = 1000 milliliters
1 milliliter = 1.000027 cubic inches

MASS (AND WEIGHT)

English to Metric
1 pound = 0.4536 kilogram
1 pound = 453.5924 grams
1 ounce = 28.3495 grams
(avdp)

Metric to English
1 kilogram = 2.2046 pounds
1 gram = 0.0022 pound
1 gram = 0.03527 ounce
(avdp)
1 milligram = 0.000035 ounce
(avdp)

Metric to Metric
1 kilogram = 1000 grams
1 gram = 1000 milligrams

ABBREVIATIONS USED FOR UNITS OF MEASUREMENT

Word	*Abbreviation*	*Word*	*Abbreviation*
avoirdupois	avdp	liter	l
centimeter	cm	meter	m
cubic centimeter	cc	micron	μ or mu
cubic inch	cu in.	mile	mi.
degree Centigrade	C	milligram	mg
degree Fahrenheit	F	milliliter	ml
fluid	fl	millimeter	mm
foot	ft	millimicron	mμ

gallon	gal	ounce	oz
gram	g	pint	pt
inch	in.	pound	lb
kilogram	kg	quart	qt
kilometer	km	yard	yd

Prefix in Metric System	Meaning
mega	1,000,000
kilo	1,000
centi	.01
milli	.001
micro	.000001

TEMPERATURE

$1°C = 1.8°F$		$1°F = 5/9°C$	
Centigrade to Fahrenheit		*Fahrenheit to Centigrade*	
−273.18	−459.72	−400	−240
−250	−418	−300	−184.5
−200	−328	−200	−129
−150	−238	−100	− 73.3
−100	−148	− 40	− 40
− 50	− 58	0	− 17.3
0	+ 32	20	− 6.7
10	+ 50	32	0
20	+ 68	50	+ 10
30	+ 86	70	+ 21.1
50	+122	100	+ 37.8
100	+212	150	+ 65.6
150	+302	200	+ 93.3
200	+392	500	+260
500	+932	1000	+537.8
1000	+1832	2000	+1093.3
2000	+3632		
3000	+5432		

CONVERSION FORMULAS

$$C = 5/9(F-32)$$
$$F = 9/5C + 32$$